Faerie Trails And Traveller Tales

Bob Knight

dp

First published in 2018 by Deveron Press

An imprint of Ayton Publishing Limited,

Hillhead of Ardmiddle, Turriff

www.aytonpublishing.co.uk

ISBN 978-1-910601-46-4

This book has been a long time in the making, and along the way I've had help and been inspired by many people. My immediate family, of course, but my mother's family, the Stewarts and McDonalds, have been the major influence on every part of my life. Quite simply, I am a Stewart in all but name.

As a singer and songwriter, many of the stories have been based on my songs; the stories behind the songs that tell what a three or four minute song can't. The ghost stories are mostly family stories I heard as a child, while others have been collected from cousins in the last few years. Thanks to everyone who contributed stories – you know who you are. I am very grateful, and proud, that you shared them with me, and perhaps through me, to the wider world.

Lastly, some stories are fiction, owing their existence purely to my imagination, and yet, nobody sails through life unaffected by those around us. There are traces of those I have known and loved in my stories and songs. Your inspiration was, and will always be valued.

To my son, Robert Knight, who keeps my feet on the ground, and asks me the pertinent questions, and often, impertinent ones too. For his skills as proof reader, and editor, and his suggestions for improvements, he has my grateful thanks.

To Cally, at Deveron Press, thank you for offering to publish my stories, thus giving me the chance to share them with a wider public. I also thank you for your advice, forbearance, and editorial guidance. I am very grateful.

Bob Knight
March, 2018.

CONTENTS

1. Footsteps On The Stairs
2. The Dark Stranger
3. The Faery Glen
4. The Fermer's Wife
5. The Go-Between
6. The Haunted Hotel
7. The Impudent Wee Snotter
8. The Man That Never Grew Auld
9. Mrs McFarlane
10. The Queen O' Swans (Walker Dam)
11. The Running Man
12. The Tinker's Kiss
13. The Haunted Bagpipes
14. Twa Ferm Loons
15. I Saw Her On The Bus
16. The Gray Lady O' Lumphanan
17. Twa Herts Entwined
18. The Oncoming Light
19. The Castle
20. The Perfume Jar
21. The Ground She Walks Upon
22. The Embrace
23. The Wrang Hand
24. My Dear Aul Frien
25. Ashypelt
26. The Psychic

1. FOOTSTEPS ON THE STAIRS

I was told this story by one of my cousins, D..... after I asked him about it a short while ago. I wanted him to remind me of the details, because I vaguely remembered some of the story from when I was a bairn, so it must have made a fair impression for me to still remember after all this time. It dates from the early 1950's, and unlike quite a few stories of its type, there is an ending that perhaps goes some way to explain the mystery.

After the Second World War, housing was very difficult to find. Thousands of soldiers were returning from the war, demobbed from the army, looking for jobs and a better way of life. Ordinary working class people often lived in squalid, overcrowded conditions which we would consider intolerable in these more enlightened times. The British government had embarked on a massive house-building programme after the war, but at the time of this story, accommodation was still scarce. My cousin lived, with others of his family, in a building, which had seen better days, and was split into smaller apartments.

The location was in the Auld Toon of Stonehaven, just a stone's throw from the harbour. The building itself was an old town house, now demolished, adjoining the clock tower, but fortunately the ancient clock tower was not torn down along with much of the Auld Toon, and is still to be seen.

His family, mother, father, some of his brothers and their wives all lived in the house, which was on two or three floors. The rooms were separated into apartments or bed-sits, as it was a large family, and because of this, it was a fair while before they realised something wasn't quite right about the house.

Often, at any time of the day or night, footsteps could be heard on the stairs. Being a large family, and living in separate parts of the house, there were a lot of comings and goings, so at first nobody paid much attention to them. Gradually they began to realise that all the footsteps couldn't be accounted for by family comings and goings, especially the ones to be heard late at night. Sitting by the fireside, or lying in bed, footsteps could be heard mounting the old creaking stairs, and stopping outside the door, but nobody ever knocked or tried to enter. After a while, they continued on their way, up to the next landing. Some of the family, bolder than others, would go to the door and open it to see who was there, but there was never anyone, or anything to be seen. On other occasions, when the door was opened, the footsteps seemed to run up to the next landing, like someone fleeing from the light, but again, nothing could be seen. On the face of it, it seemed a pretty harmless ghost, but events were soon to take a more sinister turn.

One night, D----- who was just a teenager at the time,

had been out and arrived home late, almost on the stroke of midnight. He opened the front door, and closed it behind him, and made to start up the stairs, but realised there was someone standing on the landing above him. At first he though it was one of his brothers, but as he looked, he could see in the dim light that the figure was so tall that its head seemed to disappear into the stairwell of the landing above. Thinking it could be his own shadow, he moved this way and that to test his theory, but the black shadow didn't move, and remained there, blocking his way upstairs.

'As I looked at it, it seemed tae lean forward, its feet still on the landing, but wi the top o' its body slowly driftin doon the stairs tae me. I couldnae move, paralysed with fear - I wis jist a young laddie, and I'm nae ashamed tae say I must have fainted, passed oot wi the fear o' it. I dinna ken how lang I lay there, but I woke up still terrified, and in my panic I made for the nearest door. I burst intae the room and landed in the middle o' the bed. My sister-in-law screamed as I landed between her and my brither,' related D....., laughing. 'Oh, I can laugh aboot it noo, bit it wisna sae funny at the time.'

It wasn't just D----- who had encounters with this more frightening entity though. Other members of the family met, and learned to avoid it too.

'It was a bad yin,' another of his brothers told me recently. 'If it caught you on the stairs, it would crush you

7

against the wall, so you could hardly move or breathe.'

After the family had lived there for a while, the local council applied for a compulsory purchase order as they intended to demolish the building along with a fair bit of the Auld Toon. Eventually the day came when the family had all but moved out. There was no furniture in any of the rooms, the upper apartments were vacated and empty and D----- was on the bottom floor getting ready to leave, when he heard footsteps on the stairs. Determined to get to the bottom of the mystery, he chased the footsteps right up to the top floor, but there was nothing there. Just the desolate empty rooms.

The footsteps had been heard by all of the family members at one time or another, so it can't be blamed on the over active imagination of just one person. However, there was a bizarre twist, a follow up to the story, which you may find of some interest. When the council workers eventually moved in to demolish the building, work had to be halted when they made a truly shocking discovery. Under a fireplace on the ground floor, two skeletons were discovered, one of a young woman. This is a matter of fact – it was in all the local newspapers at the time. The identity of the skeletons was never discovered. Was there a connection between the footsteps on the stairs and the skeletons under the fireplace? We can only speculate and wonder.

2. THE DARK STRANGER

In the folklore of North East Scotland, there are many stories of the Devil. Especially common, are tales linking the Devil with Bennachie; that well-known mountain and landmark, which can be see from vast swathes of Aberdeenshire. However, while my story is indeed about the Devil, the setting is the graveyard of 'The Mither Kirk' of St Nicholas in Aberdeen City Centre.

Just a few years ago, in the springtime, before the days had grown to the full measure of summer, a young man by the name of Wullie was having a drink with some friends in that well-known city pub, 'Ma Cameron's.' After a few pints of beer with his friends, Wullie decided to take his leave as he had some things to attend to at home, and made the decision that was to change his life. He took a short cut through the kirkyard of St Nicholas.

Now, it has to be said that Wullie was a most unfortunate man. He had been born with a deformity of the spine, which gave him a hunchback and bent his body so out of shape that at times he hardly looked like a human at all. It couldn't be hidden, or disguised in any way, and poor Wullie had grown up to the taunts and rebukes of strangers, and even of his school-mates, for as we know, children can be very cruel. Despite his bent and twisted body, Wullie was not a bent and twisted man and never complained about his infirmities and deformities. He had a good heart and was always ready to lend a helping hand to a friend or stranger.

So, on that fateful evening, Wullie took a short cut through St Nicholas kirkyard. The low sunshine was filtering through the budding trees and Wullie was just thinking to himself what a bonny evening it was when a tall, dark man stepped out from between the gravestones into his path.

'Christ, fit a fear ye gave me, jumpin oot on a body', Wullie exclaimed.

'Don't call me that,' the tall dark man said abruptly.

Wullie looked him up and down. A queer looking mannie was Wullie's first thoughts. Black, black, hair and eyes, and a pale thin face; dressed entirely in black.

'He lookit a bittie like a vampire in the pictures,' as Wullie later described him.

'I'm sorry sir, nae insult intended,' said Wullie, as stepped to one side, so as not to block the stranger's path.

'How very civil of you,' said the stranger, 'when in fact it was I who blocked your path.'

'Weel, it's clear noo, so nay need tae worry about it, I'll jist be on my wye hame. Good evening tae ye then,' said Wullie stepping back on to the path to leave.

Once again the stranger blocked his path.

'Just hold on a moment,' the stranger said. 'Although I mean no offence, I can't help but notice that terrible

10

deformity you suffer from. It must be an awful burden to carry though life.'

'Aye, aye, it's nae very great,' agreed Wullie, 'bit I jist think tae mysel, there's aye some puir cratur worse aff than me, so I dinna let it bother me ower much. I'm used tae it, it's my burden and it's nae use in grumblin' tae ither folk aboot my problems.'

'My, my, you're a remarkable chappie, polite and cheery, for all that life has handed you such a raw deal.'

'Weel, thank ye sir, that's affa kind o' ye tae say that, bit ye jist hiv tae get on wi life, ye canna keep on thinkin aboot whit micht hae been.'

'Never the less, I think you deserve better. Now don't let me detain you any longer, for I too have much to do this evening.'

As Wullie passed by, the stranger patted him three times on the back. Wullie just dismissed the gesture as the stranger being friendly and walked on.

'Remember me in the morning,' the stranger called after him, which Wullie thought was a strange thing to say.

But the whole incident had been strange, so Wullie thinking nothing more of it went home, did the few jobs he had intended and then to bed.

The next morning, when the alarm clock rang as usual, Wullie threw the bedcovers aside and sat up, swinging his feet out of bed and onto the floor. He sat there, still

11

drowsy from sleep, thinking for a few moments, puzzled. He slowly realised that something strange and wonderful had just happened. All his life, the act of getting out of bed had been a slow and painful one, but this morning there was no pain and he couldn't understand it.

Wullie eventually stood up to go to the bathroom, but once again, there was no pain, and then, miracle of miracles, he realised he was standing up straight. Straight, straight and tall! He wasn't bent and twisted anymore. He rushed through to the bathroom, stripping off his T-shirt as he went, and looked in the mirror. Where his misshapen and twisted hump had been, there was just a normal, straight back. His spine had somehow cured itself in the night.

Wullie thought he must be dreaming – miracles didn't happen in Aberdeen – only in strange foreign places in ancient times, but here he undeniably was, standing in front of the mirror with no hump.

'Remember me in the morning,' the words of the dark stranger in the graveyard suddenly came back to him. Could this be what he meant? It must be, it was the only thing that made any sense and in an attempt to understand the miraculous events of the morning, Wullie decided that the man had been an angel. He'd almost forgotten the man, or angel, patting him on the back three times and calling after him to be remembered in the morning but now it all made some kind of insane sense. Wullie, never a religious man, nevertheless offered up a silent prayer of thanks to the unnamed powers of the universe for his personal miracle.

Wullie spent the better part of the day wandering about the city, looking at it with new eyes; delighted by how much he could see that he had never seen before. The buildings on Union Street were beautiful, and each new architectural detail high up on the buildings amazed him.

In his former state, bent almost double, his view of life had mainly consisted of the pavement, and the ground levels of the buildings he passed each day. Now he had a new perspective and Wullie wandered about the town like a tourist, occasionally catching a glimpse of his own reflection in the shop windows and realising with a thrill that what he saw was really him.

He did a bit of shopping, buying himself new clothes, for as he dressed that morning he realised that the clothes of his old life no longer fitted. Funny, he mused to himself that his misshapen body had required clothes with no shape, but now he could buy shirts and a jacket that actually fitted.

Later, when he got back home, he cooked himself something to eat and dressed in his new clothes made his way back into the city centre heading for Ma Cameron's. A few of his friends were sitting and standing at the bar and Wullie joined them. At first, being used to his former appearance, they didn't recognise him. Oh, they thought he looked familiar right enough but couldn't quite place him until he told them who he was.

'It's me boys, Wullie, d'ye nae ken me?' he asked. To say they were amazed would be a screaming understatement. Questions rained down on him thick and fast, for let's face it, it *was* a miracle. From a stooped and twisted hunchback to a tall upright young man overnight was almost beyond comprehension. Wullie still couldn't believe it himself, so how much harder must it be for his friends? He bought them all a drink to celebrate his good fortune and recounted the events of the night before, concluding with his opinion that the dark stranger must have been an angel, or some divine emissary to have such miraculous supernatural powers to cure him. There was great speculation amongst his friends, with much good-natured debate and banter raging back and forth.

There was one there who was not so pleased with Wullie's good fortune and wished that it had been *him* who had been delivered of a miracle. He was pleased enough for Wullie, but his envy knew no bounds.

Johnny, 'The Doo,' a nickname derived from his affliction, had what was known as a pigeon chest, a deformity of the rib cage that was almost the reverse of Wullie's former hump. Unlike Wullie he had never come to terms with his condition and had gone through life cursing all and sundry. He was always complaining about this and that, never content with, or grateful for any help offered, consumed with jealousy and envy for those who he seen as better off than

14

himself.

On hearing Wullie's story Johnny resolved to go to the kirkyard of St Nicholas at the same time as Wullie had the previous night. So, he sat there, in the midst of all this joy, nursing his one miserable drink, biding his time, telling himself that he deserved a miracle just as much as 'Humpy Wullie,' for that, most uncharitably, was how he had always thought of his 'friend'. As the time drew closer he slipped away quietly, some might say 'sleekitly' and made for the kirkyard of St Nicholas.

Unlike the previous evening the weather had changed and for the worse. Cloudy and overcast, it seemed almost dark when he reached the kirkyard. He ventured in, looking for the tall dark stranger but the place was empty. He walked all the way through the graveyard, coming out onto Union Street at the far side and then walked back again to the Schoolhill entrance but the place was still empty and deserted.

He thought for a moment, furious that the angel hadn't put in an appearance. Cursing his luck and everything else in his life, he retraced his steps going back into the kirkyard for one last try. It had started to rain and the place was even darker and gloomier than before. He skirted the kirk and slowly made his way towards the Union Street gate when he finally saw a tall, dark man, pale faced, dressed in black standing between the ancient gravestones.

'Weel,' he said, 'are ye jist gaun tae stand there, are ye nae gaun tae block my path like ye did wi Wullie last night?'

'My dear fellow, I have no intention of blocking your path. Please be on your way,' the dark stranger said, ignoring Johnny.

'Whit? Dae ye think I've been wanderin up and doon here for the last twenty minutes for nithin. Ye performed a miracle for "Humpy Wullie," last night, so is it askin too much that ye dae the same for me?' he demanded.

'There is a world of difference between last night and tonight. Now, please be on your way,' the tall dark stranger said with a growing hint of irritation in his voice.

'Ach!' Johnny spat out, 'Wullie said ye were an angel, bit I doot he got that a' wrang. Ye're jist a big lanky creep that hings aboot in graveyards. Ye're jist a fraud, nae an angel.'

'You're right in some ways my good man, it's been a long, long time since anyone has thought of me as an angel.'

'I kent it, nae use for nithin,' said the bad tempered fool.

'I see that you too suffer from a terrible, hideous deformity. Is that what they call a pigeon chest?' the dark man enquired, pointing at Johnny's chest.

'Aye, fit aboot it, and fit's it tae you?' Johnny snapped.

'I'm terribly sorry, I meant no offence. Perhaps you should be grateful that you don't have such a terrible, burden as your good friend William?' he offered.

'William… oh, ye mean Humpy Wullie? Aye that's true, but my chest is jist as bad as his hump, and I did nithin tae deserve it either. It's ruined my life, stopped me getting jobs, women winna look at me, it's jist affa. Can ye nae help me?'

'I can only say again that you should be grateful that your affliction is not as bad as William's,' repeated the stranger, gently patting the impatient fool on the back as if in sympathy.

'Look, here I am, standin in the pissin rain, cauld and miserable, spikken shite wi an idiot. Fuck off, oot o my road, I'm gaun hame, I've got better things tae dee wi my time,' and he stomped off in disgust.

The dark stranger watched him as he left, shaking his head with resignation.

'Remember me in the morning,' he said quietly, with a wicked smile.

The next day dawned, grey and cold, just as wet and miserable as the evening before. Lying in bed, feeling stiff and sore, Johnny finally decided to get up. As he tried to get out of bed a deep, agonising pain in his back made him cry out; sweat ran down his forehead and face. Finally, with great effort, he got out of bed but fell over and struggled for some time to get back to his feet, finally managing only to find himself unable to stand up straight. Stooped, and doubled up with pain, he made his way to the bathroom to investigate the cause of this fresh agony. What he saw in the mirror made him scream with rage, horror and despair. There upon his back was the most enormous hairy hump, twisting and bending him out of shape.

For almost an hour he ranted, raged and railed against the world, wept and wailed, asking himself, God, and any who came into his fevered mind, why him? What had he done to deserve this? Wullie he cursed most of all. It was his fault for telling him about the angel in the first place. He was no angel, more like a demon he thought, finally remembering the words of the man in the kirkyard.

'Perhaps you should be grateful that you don't have such a terrible deformity as your friend William?' and, 'It's a long, long time since anyone has thought of me as an angel.'

Johnny finally understood with growing horror and self-realisation that what had happened was all due to his own envy, jealousy, and bad temper; that he had brought this calamity on himself. The dark stranger *was* indeed an angel, but a dark and fallen angel. Lucifer, cast out of heaven, the devil himself.

3. THE FAERY GLEN

The first thing that has to be said is that Scottish faeries bear no resemblance to English fairies. Whilst the English fairy is a tiny flying creature, more like a large humming bird in size, Scottish faeries are only slightly smaller in stature than humans. They could in fact pass for human, and if the truth be told, they often do when they make the occasional foray into our domain.

Throughout all the ages there have been certain places shunned by humans. These places have gained a quiet reputation amongst the local populations who avoid them whenever possible. Those who venture in, the adventurous, the unwary, or the plain stupid, often return unscathed, but sometimes, they are marked for life in some strange way, or disappear. Some return many years later, thinking they have been gone a few days only, for time runs on a different track in the land of the faeries. There are many such places in Scotland; quiet, lonely places where the realm of the faeries comes ominously close to ours

From the time she was a small child, Sarah's mother had told her stories of the Faery Glen. Implicit in her stories was the warning; never, ever, go into Faery Glen under any circumstances, for danger lay there to snare the unwary and cause those foolish enough to enter untold misery and even death. Her mother and aunts told her other stories too. Tales of dragons and magical lands far across the sea, stories of handsome princes and silly younger sons, of treasure chests and fierce pirates who sailed upon the sea; but always there was the dark tales of the Faery Glen.

In time Sarah grew up to be a tall, beautiful young woman with long golden hair and sparkling blue eyes. Her skin was pale and clear with just a few freckles sprinkled across her straight little nose. Her full, sensual lips gave a hint of the passion that was held within and her figure, although slim, was womanly. She was the centre of attention for the sons of local lairds and rich merchants, who would marry her in an instant if she would only say yes.

But at just seventeen, Sarah was in no hurry to marry and leave her parents whom she adored. As an only child, they had lavished all their love and attention on Sarah, and she returned their love in full measure. She was everything they could have wished for in a daughter; good natured, intelligent, modest and demure, but; and there's always a 'but'; for no person who is too perfect may be allowed to exist upon our world, this paragon had one fatal flaw. She was thrawn, or in other words, stubborn. Whatever she was told, or asked to do, she did the opposite, which would in time, lead to her downfall.

On a bright summer morning of her seventeenth year,

Sarah rose early and after breakfast decided to go for a walk. It was a beautiful day and she wandered, here and there, daydreaming and not really paying much attention to where she was going. After a time she found herself on the edge of a dark wood and realised, with a thrill of fear, that she was on the edge of Faery Glen.

Her mother's words came back to her as she remembered the dire warnings given and the stories she had been told of the dangers within. She hesitated for a moment or two and summoning up her courage, stepped onto the narrow footpath that led into the dark wood. Soon she was lost to the sight of the outside world but since nobody was there to see, it didn't really matter.

She had soon walked through the thickest part of what turned out to be a very small wood and the landscape opened up before her into meadows and parkland with only the occasional wooded area scattered here and there. She thought the place was enchanting, which was closer to the truth than she knew. Wild flowers grew in profusion, birds sang, butterflies fluttered, bees buzzed and she caught the occasional glimpse of shy, silent deer amongst the trees.

All day long she wandered in the warm sunshine, losing track of time, distracted by each new delight the Faery Glen had to offer. Soon she had picked a large bunch of wildflowers to take home to her mother but suddenly realised that it was getting late. By the position of the sun she could tell it was early afternoon and she had wandered so much further than she had intended. Her little feet were sore and she was tired, so reluctantly she turned for home, resolved to return to Faery Glen another day.

Skirting a small stand of trees she came upon a gurgling burn, which she couldn't remember seeing earlier, and suddenly realising that she was thirsty, sat down upon the bank in the shade of some trees and cupping her hands, drank some of the cool, clear water. She sat there for a time, resting and daydreaming but with her early rise that morning and the warm sunshine conspiring against her, she fell into a sleep. Eyes watched her from the darkness below the trees as she slept, and admired her beauty... she was not alone.

She dreamed, and in her dream a young man came, surely the most handsome prince of any fable. He spoke to her and taking her hand, walked with her in the meadow. He was the most imposing man she had ever seen, tall and dark, with dark twinkling eyes, richly dressed in cloth of a golden hue. By his side hung a broadsword and tethered to a nearby tree his white horse stood patiently, cropping the grass as it grazed. He mounted, swinging up easily into the saddle and reaching down, lifted her onto his lap. It seemed the most natural thing in the world and she made no protest except to ask.

'Whaur are you taking me sir?'

'Tae my castle, whaur thou shall be my queen, bonny Sarah,' he replied.

She asked no more, for at that moment she could think of nothing else which would please her more. The horse broke into a gallop and with the wind blowing through her hair she relaxed, safe in the arms of her prince, and closed her eyes. After a while he spoke again.

'Look my love, see my castle, soon it will be thine and the hairts o' a' within, for they shall love thee as I dae,' he declared.

Sarah said nothing, content to be in the arms of her prince, but thought the castle was the most beautiful castle she had ever seen and longed to be within the safety of its walls.

The great oak gates opened as they approached, the horse's hooves clattering noisily on the cobblestones as they entered the courtyard within. A groom came forward and took the reins as they dismounted and Sarah was swept on the arm of her prince into the cool shade of the castle hall.

'Bring us wine if thou please,' he commanded.

As if by magic a servant appeared and placed wine and glasses on the table.

'Come my lass,' he said, 'let us drink tae oor love and tae thee, my Queen,' and he poured her a glass of the finest claret in all the land.

As she sipped, her lips wet with the redness of the

wine, he impulsively stooped and drank the wine from her lips with a kiss. She had never kissed a man before and she was soon lost in the wonder of it all as he returned to kiss her again and again. Such a strange thing she thought, such a strange feeling, but she returned his kiss with a newly awakened passion. All the while he stroked her long beautiful hair and between kisses whispered words of love in her dainty ears.

After a while he stood and, taking her hands in his, raised her from the chair.

'Come my love, it's time for thee tae become my Queen,' he announced, and slipping an arm around her waist, he led her from the room and up a grand stairway which led to the upper floors of the castle.

In a willing daze she allowed herself to be led into a sumptuous apartment with magnificent wall hangings, where candles burned and a light fragrance of flowers and perfume filled the air. Everything was of the best; silk, satin, and damask, the finest linens were on the bed. He kissed her again and she returned his kisses in full measure as he laid her down gently upon the wondrous soft bed.

In her dream she felt a pain at her very core, momentary and sharp, but so very, very sweet. She didn't waken and slept on. As the day dwindled, the heat of the afternoon began to dissipate and she woke naturally from her sleep and dreams, but it was no pleasant awakening for

Sarah. Much to her despair she discovered that her clothing was in disarray, her bodice gaping wide, her dress and petticoats scarcely covering her modesty. She burst into tears, all the while buttoning her bodice and re-arranging her clothes, looking round frantically to see who had done this thing, but nobody was there. She was alone, the mood of the day had changed and the birds now seemed to sing less sweetly. The bees no longer buzzed, the warming sun was behind a cloud. She cursed her stupidity for not heeding her mother's warning about the dangers of Faery Glen as she made her frightened and lonely way home.

It never entered Sarah's head to keep what happened in Faery Glen a secret, for she loved her parents and held no secrets from them. On hearing what happened her mother burst into tears, which was only natural, for she adored Sarah and lived to protect her child from the wickedness of the world.

Now Sarah had indeed come to harm and placed herself in danger by doing exactly what her mother had always warned her not to do. Her mother's great ambitions and hopes for the lovely Sarah, who was surely destined to marry a rich and noble husband now seemed in ruins, for Sarah, by her headstrong actions had put all these hopes and dreams in jeopardy.

Her mother told her father, who ranted and raged against the world and for the first time in his life shouted in anger at his daughter. He vowed dire revenge if he ever laid hands on the man who had done this thing, knowing deep in his heart as he said it that no man was to blame. But he ranted and raved all the same, for it made him feel slightly better about this vile thing which he could do nothing about.

Sarah wept floods of bitter tears for her situation and for the distress she had caused her parents – but being young and innocent, how could she have forseen the repercussions of her foray into the Faery Glen?

Apart from the loss of that which could never be replaced, Sarah was in perfect health. She had no other injuries from her experience. Once she and her parents had come to terms with what had happened in Faery Glen, daily life in the household returned to normality. Her mother prayed and prayed that no lasting harm had befallen her child, but her prayers were not answered. Her hopes were dashed as it soon became obvious that Sarah had not escaped so lightly after all.

One fine morning Sarah was overcome with nausea, and, with a sinking heart, her mother finally knew that her prayers had not been answered and that her Sarah would soon be a mother. As the months passed Sarah grew bigger and bigger. She hid herself away from the eyes of strangers, for in those days it was a shameful thing to be pregnant with no husband.

The year wore on, and Christmas and New Year

passed, with little to celebrate, and finally in the month of March, Sarah knew her time had come. After much pain and struggle she was delivered of a beautiful baby girl. Sarah fell asleep, holding the child in her arms, exhausted by her efforts.

When Sarah awoke, her mother was sitting by the bed, the child wrapped in a shawl, rocking gently back and forth, 'cooing,' soothing sounds to the babe. Aware that Sarah had woken, her mother finally spoke.

'Sarah, my darling, this bairnie is a faery lass, we daur nae keep her here,' she said quietly with fear and anxiety in her eyes. 'She will bring ill-luck an' great danger tae us a', for her faither will surely come tae claim his ain.'

'Aye, I ken mother, but there's little we can dae aboot that. If he comes for her, then he comes for her.'

Woken by their voices the baby started to cry. Sarah took the babe in her arms again, cradling her to her breast to sooth and suckle.

Her mother's words proved all too prophetic, for that same night, after dark, as the hour was growing very late, there came a thunderous rattling and knocking at the door. Given the lateness of the hour the whole household was in bed but the rattling and knocking at the door grew louder and more insistent until at last, Sarah's father threw open his bedroom window.

In the yard below stood a black coach, drawn by four

27

fiery tempered black horses, snorting and blowing, their iron-shod hooves striking the ground and drawing sparks from the cobble stones as if impatient to be on their way.

'In the name o' God, whit are ye knockin' at the door for at this ungodly 'oor?' he protested, knowing well enough what was afoot.

'Come doon the stairs my bonnie lass and bring to me oor bairn,' the faery prince demanded, ignoring her father's question.

Sarah, by this time had opened her window too and called back, 'No, never, ye'll tak my babe, and maybe dae us herm tae,' she spoke bravely, although very frightened.

'Open the door and let me see oor bairn. I could herm ye fae here if that was my wish,' he replied.

Sarah's mother, always realistic, was already halfway down the stairs, knowing that they could not prevent such a powerful faery being from entering. Opening the door, she curtsied and bade him enter, just as Sarah came down the stairs, closely followed by her father.

'By God sir, ye've got some impudence comin tae my door in the middle o' the nicht efter whit ye've done. Hiv ye nae shame man?' Sarah's father spat out.

'For my transgressions sir, I apologise maist sincerely, but I have come here this nicht tae mak amends if possible, and tae see oor bairnie,' he said turning, smiling to Sarah who carried the babe in her arms.

28

'Ye can see her, bit yer nae gettin her,' said Sarah defiantly.

'Oh Sarah, my queen, ye hae little understanding o' whit being born wi faery blood means,' he said. 'I canna leave her here wi you in this mortal realm. Ye're lives are but a blink, a season, that flares briefly like a flame in the darkness compared tae the virtual immortality that living in the domain o' the faeries will bring her. If I leave her here wi you, her life will be short compared tae ithers o' her kind. Will ye condemn her tae an untimely death?' he asked.

Sarah looked down at the babe, asleep in her arms, the tears running from her eyes and knew she could not. She stepped forward and reluctantly handed the babe to the prince, sobbing piteously.

'Sarah, ye needna pairt fae her. I promised that ye shall be my queen, and I meant it. Jist say fareweel tae yer parents, an come awa this very nicht, and bide wi me in Faery Glen.'

Sarah didn't answer for a few minutes, thinking about her reply.

'Sir, you're offer is good,' she began 'but I'll nae leave my parents tae live in Faery Glen, for I couldnae thole the thocht that I'd niver see them again.'

'Then fareweel lass, I wish ye weel, but before I tak my leave o' ye, yer fortune I will tell.'

He closed his eyes, swaying slightly as if listening to

some unheard music. After a few short minutes, he opened his dark eyes again.

'Ye'll merry a rich man, a man that's good and true until death. Twa laddies and a lass ye'll hae. Aye, ye'll hae much joy and love o' yer bairns and husband, an' it will be a good and a lang life,' he finished.

'Will I see her again?' she asked looking at the babe asleep in his arms.

'Perhaps, but I canna mak promises, for yer time rins sae quick,' he said.

He bowed to her parents, smiled at her. Taking her hand, he raised it to his lips and kissed her fingers. Turning on his heel, he swept out of the door and without looking back jumped aboard the coach. The fiery black horses needed no other signal. Within seconds the coach, prince and bairn were gone, vanished into the darkness as if they'd never existed. Sarah wept long and hard for many nights thereafter.

In time, all that the faery prince said came to pass. Sarah eventually met, fell in love with and married her rich man, good and true. She had three children who brought great joy and love as promised to Sarah, her husband and their doting grandparents. On her deathbed, some seventy years later, surrounded by the love of her children and grandchildren, Sarah lay at her life's end. It had been a good life, as prophesised by her faery prince and she would have been content to go to the realm that lies beyond death but for one thing, she longed to see her daughter, the faery princess, just once before the end.

As she hovered between this life and the next, the door of the room quietly opened and a child entered. An extraordinarily beautiful girl, dressed in cloth of gold, with long golden hair, sparkling blue eyes and a sprinkling of freckles across her straight little nose. Sarah looked at her, and even though her eyes were dimmed with age, she knew instantly that this was her daughter, her first born and her heart swelled with love and pride. The princess crossed the room, kissed her mother's brow tenderly and smiled so very sweetly.

'Oh lass, you came, you came, I thank ye,' she said, her voice tailing off.

Closing her eyes, she drifted off and was gone, content and at peace.

4. THE FERMER'S WIFE

The first time I saw her she wis walking roon the Castlegate in Aiberdeen. A fine looking lass, a bittie lost kind, wearin a raincoat an' a Fair Isle tammy. It was Friday May 26th, twa days afore the term, in 1939. Mysel, alang wi a gweed puckle o' ither lads wis lookin for a fee. Twa or three o' the loons were gien her the ee, an' yin o' them said something that wisnae affa polite. They lauched, and she blushed an' lookit awa.

'Hud yer wheesht lads, hae some respect for the lass,' I said sherpish like, an' they hid the sense tae look a bit shame-faced an' turn awa.

She lookit at me, up and doon as if thinkin, an' spoke.

'Are ye looking for a fee?' she askit.

'Aye, I am that,' I replied.

'Weel, I'm looking for a body that can turn his han' tae jist aboot onythin,' she stated, 'It's jist a wee bit placie though, wi scarce work eneuch for yin,' she went on.

'If at's the case,' I said, affa canny like, 'fit wye wid ye need me?'

'My man, the fermer, hid an accident a few month syne, an' hurtit his back. He's beddit, an' atween lookin efter him an' trying tae work the ferm I'm jist nae able tae hud it gan,' she explained. I felt a bittie sorry for her.

'Weel, I'm yer man if ye think I micht suit,' I offered.

32

She askit me aboot my last place, onny references and sic like and wi that I wis hired for the term.

We agreed tae meet up later as she hid a bit o' shoppin tae dae an' I hid tae collect my gear fae the left luggage office at the station, for I'd come in by train. I passed the time ha'in a gill wi some aul pals I met up wi at the mairket.

Come closing time, wi the efterneen afore me, I hid a stroll aboot the toon, takin in the sichts, an' michty me, some richt sichts there wis. Lassies wi faces sae pented they lookit like china dolls, an' lads wi' mousers sae thin t'wis hardly worth the bother o' growin, or gien it the name o' a moustache, bit at's fashion for ye I reflectit! Finally, I collectit my gear, an' met up wi her. I pit my case, an' few bits an' pieces in the boot o' her aul black car, for the back seat wis fair covered in broon paper parcels.

I sat in the front beside her an' watched her as she drove. She wis a handsome lookin lassie; blue een wi dark reid hair, fit they cry "auburn". Her skin wis saft an' pale, wi a few freckles on her cheeks an' nose. Nae fat, bit nae too thin neither, an' aboot twinty seven or echt, or thereaboots. We spoke noo and again tae pass the time. I telt her how I'd spent my efterneen, an' a' the sichts o' Union Street. Efter a while she said.

'Ye've been drinkin, I can smell it aff ye. I hope yer nae a boozer.'

'Nah lass,' I assured her. 'I've hid a drink or twa wi

33

some aul pals, bit nae mair. I hae a sociable dram at the term, an' at New Year, bit in atween han' I niver touch it.'

'I see, a' richt, I'm sorry if I soundit a bit sherp, bit I canna thole a man that's aye boozing.'

'Niver fear quine. Nae offence teen,' I assured her.

A few mair meenits saw us turn intae the road tae the ferm. It wisna far oot o' Aiberdeen, aboot halfwye atween the Don an' Dee. The hens in the yerd scattert in a' directions as we drove in aboot. I helpit her tae the hoose wi her parcels an' she put on the kettle for a cup o' tea, syne wint ben the hoose tae see tae her man.

'The fermer wid like tae see ye,' she said, coming back intae the room.

I followed her ben, intae the bedroom. The man wis flat oot on his back, an' nae lookin weel at a'. I shook his han', still a good grip on him for a' that, an' we spoke awa. As it turned oot, his back wisna jist hurt, it wis broken.

He telt me he'd niver walk again and he wis nae use for nithin. Weel, there wisnae muckle I could say tae that, bit I tried tae cheer him up a bittie, an' telt him I'd dae my best tae help an' tak the place in han'.

Efter we hid a cup o' tea she showed me tae the bothy far I wid be bidin. It wis a' richt, a bittie stoorie kind, bit dry an' comfortable lookin. There wis a fireplace far I could bile a kettle, a joog an' bowl for washin, a good sized bed wi a horsehair mattress, blankets an' a chair or twa for sittin.

'Fin yer settled, come ower tae the hoose for yer supper,' she said as she left me tae unpack.

Next mornin I wis up bricht an' early tae hae a look ower the place an' see whit wis needin deen. It wis a bit neglectit like, bit 'at wis tae be expectit wi jist the lassie tryin tae dee it a' hersel. I kent I wid hae tae get buckled doon stracht awa, an' I did.

Ower the next few weeks I began tae get the upper han', until finally I hid the place back tae fit it should hae bin. She niver interfered, bit jist left me tae get on wi it. I likit 'at fine, for I could niver thole a body stan'in ower me telling me first ae thing an' syne the ither. I ken fit needs deen, an' I jist get on wi it, bit at's my wye. She helpit me fae time tae time as ony fermer's wife wid dee, an' she wis a gweed help richt eneuch. Strong and sensible, I likit her fine, bit I didnae ask her help too aften. I kent she hid her han's full wi' lookin efter her man, an' deein her ain jobs aboot the place.

I got my brakfest at the hoose, an' my supper tae. Files I wid hae a word wi the fairmer, an' he wid tell me things he thocht needit deen, an' I wid tell him fit I wis deein aboot his place. He seemed contentit eneuch wi' fit I wis deein, bit I could see he wisnae makin muckle o't, an' wis fadin awa!

Efter supper, if I hid nae jobs tae dee, me an' her wid sit and listen tae the wireless, or spik a while. There wisnae muckle good news ava. It wis lookin affa like we were heidin

35

for anither war. Thon mannie Hitler wis jist itchin for a fecht. I wis only aboot fourteen, or fifteen fin the last war endit, bit I could still mind sojers comin hame wi empty sleeves an' trooser legs pinned tae their claithes. Worse still were the men wi the empty een; a' sense blawn awa by the shellin an' the sichts they'd seen. Even the lads 'at seemed aricht wid niver speak o't.

'Nah laddie, it's better forgotten,' wis aye their reply if ye askit aboot it. I didnae wint tae see 'at again, an' I didnae wint tae be a sojer neither.

Mind you, it wisnae a' doom an' gloom, an' we hid a lauch or twa as weel, bit she didnae like tae lauch too much in the hoose. I jaloused that she thocht it micht nae be richt fin her man wis lyin ben the hoose in pain. Bit by bit, an' I sweir I tried my best nae til, I began tae fa for the lassie. I likit bein' in her company, speakin wi her, lauchin wi her an' jist seein her gan aboot the place. Sometimes on the lang June an' July nichts fin she came oot tae gie me a han' an' the late sun was shinin through her reid hair, I thocht I'd niver seen onythin as bonny in my life. I wid daydream aboot her as I workit, an' watch her as she wint aboot her jobs, collectin the eggs an' sic like. I said nithin tae her for she wis a merriet woman, an' I hidnae the richt, bit I winted her mair than onythin I'd iver winted afore.

I wis workin in the barn ae day fin she come in aboot. I lookit up as she came in, her bonny face a' serious like.

36

'Can I hae a word wi ye?' she askit.

'Aye, of course ye can,' I replied, 'fit's wrang like?'

'It's a bittie awkward kind, bit I've noticed the wye ye watch me gan aboot,' she said, wringin her han's as she spoke.

'Fit aboot it?' I said quietly. 'I'm nae hermin ye, nor interferin wi ye in ony wye, an' I'm getting on wi my work,'

'If it wis jist me that's noticed it widnae be ony bother, bit ithers hiv noticed tae. Mrs Matthews, fin she came ower, and the district nurse forbye.' She named a few ither visitors tae the ferm; busybodies yin an' a'.

'Weel, it's like this lass,' I said leanin the pitchfork against the wa'. 'I watch ye because I like the look o' ye,' I said. 'Yer a bonny lass, I like yer face, yer hair, an' yer figure. I ken it's maybe wrang in some folk's een, bit I've fa'in in love wi ye.'

She opened her mou an' lookit like she wis gan tae speak, bit nithin came oot.

'Bit I'm a merriet woman,' she finally managed tae say as I stepit closer, oor bodies near touchin.

'Aye, I ken. I've tried nae til, bit I canna help it, and there ye hiv it,' I declared, and wi that I pit my airms roon her waist and pulled her fine soft body intae mine.

She tried tae push awa, bit I wis ower strong an' bent me heid tae kiss her bonny lips. She focht back, an' thinkin I'd made an affa mistake I wis jist aboot tae pull awa, fin wid ye believe it, she kissed me back. She held me ticht, her body gan a saft an' warm against mine, her lips opening an' kissin me, ivery bit as hungry as mine. We jist stood there, kissin each ither, excitement growin, until at last we baith sank doon amang the hay.

Efterwards, as she lay there in my airms, she askit me, quiet like. 'Fit are we gan tae dee noo?'

'God knows lass,' I replied. 'It's a richt mess an' nae mistake.' I felt her body grow tense against me.

'Are ye sorry it happent noo then?' she said, sounin me oot.

'Niver lass, fit wye wid I be sorry? Yer the best thing at's iver happent tae me; the best thing in my hale life.'

She relaxt again an' we lay there quietly, contentit in each ithers airms.

As the simmer wound on intae August we found ivery chance tae be thegither, an' it wis aye a delicht for me tae be in her company. Nae jist the makin love, bit being wi her, spikin tae her, sharin a table at brakfest and supper, lauchin wi her at silly things, or jist ha'in a walk roon the ferm on the lang simmer nichts fin the days work wis deen.

Almost afore we kent far we wis, the hairst wis upon us. It meant a few weeks hard, hard work as we got the crops cut and stookit, syne helpit oot on the neebours ferms, as they hid helpit us. For a' the hard work, we hid a great sense o' satisfaction fin it wis a' ower an' done wi. Bit there's aye

38

something tae spile it, an' though athin on the ferm wis "rosie," in the world ootside, the news wis aboot as bad as it could get.

Thon Hitler cheil hid sent his armies intae Poland, an' for a' the huffin an' puffin o' Britain and France, he widnae step back, an' so war wis declared at the beginnin' o' September. I kent I widnae hae tae gyang intae the army unless I wintit tae. Efter a', somebody hid tae work the land, an' produce the crops tae feed the country, an' mine wis a "reserved occupation".

So, life wint on, much the same as it hid a' through the autumn o' 1939. I workit the ferm, an' seen tae a'thing 'at needit deen, and ivery mornin' an' nicht, there wis her. Files we wid hae a bit o' fun, ither times we wid jist enjoy each ither's company in a mair innocent wye, spikin aboot the days events, or listenin tae the news on the wireless. The news o' the war seemed tae be gan fae bad tae worse, 'til at last we damn near stoppit listenin tae it for fear o' fit micht gyang wrang next.

There wis anither clood in oor sky; something 'at neither o' us wis happy aboot, an' that wis her man. He wisnae weel an' gettin worse, an' she wis fair rackit wi guilt aboot him. Tae tell the truth, I likit him fine an' wis hairt sorry him mysel', bit I hiv tae admit, I likit her an affa lot better, an' fin I wis wi her, nithin else mettert. I ken it's nae excuse, bit we jist hid tae get on wi it and mak the best o' a

39

bad lot.

The fine simmer hid dwindled tae autumn; the days still maistly clear, but the nichts were fair drawin in and frosty forbye. We saw October oot, syne intae November. Ae nicht she wis lookin at me a bit queer like, affa worriet an' uneasy wi hersel'.

'Fit's wrang lass?' I askit. 'Somethins up, yer nae jist yersel.'

'Och, I've got something tae say, bit it'll brak my hert tae say it,' she said, nae meetin my ee. My mou wint dry, an' I said nithin for a meenit.

'Fit is't lass?' I got oot at last.

'Weel, it's like this,' she startit. 'Folk are spikin aboot us. Fin I gyang intae the village shops, they stop spikin fin I come in. Or, I can see them a' thegither, an' aye lookin my wye fin they think I dinna notice.'

'Bliddy gossips,' I raged, 'aul biddies wi nithin better tae dee.'

'Aye, I ken, bit dinna forget I'm a merriet woman. It's creatin a scandal. The meenister even spoke tae me aboot it, bit I telt him it wis a' havers,' she said.

'Weel, fit dae ye wint me tae dee?' I askit, half kennin fit wis comin.

'I think ye'll need tae leave – tak anither fee,' she said, brakin doon an' greetin like a bairn.

'Hush lass, dinna worry. Ye ken I'll dee onything tae

40

keep ye fae herm.'

'I ken, an' I dinna wint ye tae leave, bit I canna see ony ither wye oot o't,' she grat.

So, in the end we agreed, efter a lot o' discussion aboot fit wis richt and wrang, wi me ragin an' her greetin, that we wid separate for a while. For the sake o' her 'good name,' an' 'respectability', we wid gyang oor ain wyes, an' I wid tak anither fee, hopin it wid pit an end tae the gossip. It micht hae been a' settled, bit 'at didnae stop us gan ower it again an again for the next few nichts, tryin tae find a wye oot o' it mair tae oor likin, bit we couldnae mak a better o't. It wis a miserable time for us baith.

Twa or three days afore the term I got my few 'bits and bobs,' thegither, an' efter ha'in a last look aboot the place far I hid bin sae happy, bit noo jist hairtbroken, she drove me intae Aiberdeen in her aul car. I can tell ye noo, the pairtin was lang an' sair, an' I'm nae ashamed tae say there wis tears in my een as I watcht her drive awa. I wid write tae her fin I wis settled, an' keep in touch. It wis a hard, hard thing, an' we didnae even like tae speak aboot it, bit we baith kent her man wis nae lang for this world. Maybe in a year or twa, fin things hid come tae their natural conclusion, we wid be thegither again, bit until sic times we hid tae mak the best o't. Little did I ken that it wid be mony a lang year afore I saw her bonny face again.

My new fee wis a fair bit oot o' Aiberdeen, an' aboot

thirty odd mile awa fae her place, so there wisnae onny chance tae see her, even on a Sunday. I wrote tae tell her far I wis, an' she wrote back jist afore the new year, wishin me a happy new year for 1940, bit for a' her wishes, there wisnae muckle happiness gan aboot. It wis a hard cauld winter, bit I jist got my heid doon an' workit an' slept, workit an' slept. My hairt wisnae in it, an' the news fae the rest o' the country wis nane better. The war wisnae gan weel for us, an' things hid hit a bit o' a lull, fit they wid later cry "The Phoney War", bit phoney though it micht hae been, we were still a' worriet aboot fit the New Year micht bring.

The fairmer fairly kept oor noses tae the grindstone, but 'at suited me jist fine, for I didnae wint ower muckle time tae think aboot oor situation. We swappit a few mair letters ower the following months, an' it wis aye grand tae get her news. I could jist aboot hear her voice spikin fin I read her words. There wis niver onything o' great importance tae tell bit it wis important tae us I suppose, jist 'at she missed me, an' fit a struggle it wis wi'oot me. I couldnae help bit worry aboot her.

Ae day I got back tae the bothy tae find there wis anither letter for me, bit it wisnae fae her, it wis fae the King! I wis invited tae join His Majesty's army, an' report by the specified date. I suppose I could hae gotten oot o't, bein a ferm worker, bit I wisnae carin muckle aboot onythin, I wis ower scunnert, an' jist let mysel be swept alang by it a'.

A few weeks later I wis in the Gordon Highlanders, trainin tae be a sojer, syne fully trained, we wis waitin for orders tae jine oor division, an' the big fecht. First we were sent by train tae a camp somewye in the sooth o' England, an' it wis there that her letter caught up wi me. I damn near fell through the fleer fin I read that I wis the faither o' a healthy wee laddie. I never even suspectit she wis gan tae hae a bairn, bit it a' addit up fin I thocht aboot it.

If I hid been there fin the bairn wis born, a' body wid hiv kent it wis mine, bit noo, even though the fairmer wis beddit, there wid be some doot, an' the bairn wid hae the fairmers name. It wis an affa stigma in thae days tae hae the name, 'bastard'. I applied for compassionate leave tae get hame tae her an' the bairn, bit wis refused, for we were on oor wye tae France within days. I wrote tae her afore we left, bit couldnae say far I wis gan or nithin. Noo I hid a double reason tae see her again, bit I didnae ken as I wrote, that my war wid soon come tae an end at a place cried St. Valery, an' that it wid be a lang, lang time afore I saw her or my bairn.

* * *

Fin I came hame efter the war, ferm work wis hard tae get. Maist o' the ferms still hid the land girls, an' I thocht it wis time for a change onywye. I got a job drivin the buses for Alexander's, the main bus company servin the country areas o' Aiberdeenshire, an' got lodgins nae far fae the bus depot jist aff Holburn Street in Aiberdeen. I seen settled back intae

43

civilian life - nae that I'd hid a great military career, hivin spent maist o' the war, a prisoner in Germany.

Ae day, yin o' the ither drivers wis nae weel, an' I wis shifted on tae his bus route. It meant I wid be passin through the village nearest tae her ferm ivery day. I hoped I micht see her, bit kent it wid be a miracle in the few short meenits I wis passin through. Efter four or five days I'd kinda gien up hope an' telt mysel nae to be sae daft. Syne ae day I hid tae drap aff some parcels at the Post Office, an' as I got back on the bus an' wis gan tae drive aff, a woman came teerin' oot o the grocer's store, waving at me tae wait. She got on, a' breathless, an' oor een met. It wis her! My hairt wis thumpin sae much I thocht it wid burst. I could hardly spik, an' finally got oot.

'Hello, it's yersel lass,' as I startit the bus rollin.

'Aye, foo are ye?' she returned.

'Nae great, bit a' the better noo for seein you,' I said.

She sat doon in the first seat beside the door, across the aisle an' a wee bittie behind me. She sat there quietly.

'I'm richt gled tae see yer hame safe,' she finally said.

'Me an' a' lass,' I said.

She got oot o' her seat a bittie early kind, an stood beside me, keeping her voice low so the ither passengers widnae hear.

'Ye winna ken I s'pose, bit my man passed awa aboot four year syne,' she telt me.

44

'Nah, I niver kent, I'm sorry tae hear it,' I said sympathetically, spierin. 'fit happent like?'

'Weel, I think he jist gave up - didnae wint tae live efter the accident. It wis pneumonia that took him awa,' she explained.

We said nithin mair, thinkin on it, bit at last the road tae her place came in view an' she spoke again, 'I think it's time ye met yer loon – if ye wint tae of course. Will ye come oot on Sunday?'

'Of course I wint tae see him, an' you tae,' I added.

'Come oot on Sunday then, come oot for yer denner,' an' wi that I pulled the bus intae the side o' the road tae let her aff.

As she wis getting aff, she turned tae me, tears in her een an' said, 'There wis niver a day... niver a single day in a' the years, bit I thocht o' you an' me,' an' wi that she wis aff the bus an' rinnin, heid doon, up the track tae her ferm.

Sunday came at last, an' I hid gotten a shot o' an aul car fae a lad I kent, an' at last found mysel turning intae the road leadin tae her ferm. The years fair peeled awa as I mindit on the first time she drove me up this road. I saw her then, stan'in at the door o' the fermhoose, as bonny as she iver wis, a young laddie by her side, an' I felt happy for the first time in years. The hens scattert aboot the dusty yerd as I drove in, jist like they hid sae mony years syne, an' I could see her smilin a welcome tae me. I felt I wis hame at last.

45

5. THE GO-BETWEEN

This is another story based on a song I have written. I got the original idea for the song from the old Irish folk song, 'She Moved Through The Fair.' I thought it rather unkind of his dead love to come back as a ghost, only to tell him that he was going to die, so I thought, 'What would a modern twenty first century woman do if she was given the same opportunity?' I decided that she'd probably want him, being relatively young, to be happy and get on with his life, but wouldn't trust him to pick the right woman. Given the opportunity, she'd come back, pick his next wife and give him a nudge in the right direction.

* * *

I wis sitting in my ain hoose, deein nithing, fin somebody knockit at the door. Fin I opened the door there stood three or fower o' my aul pals. I hidna seen them for months.

'Aye, aye boys, fit like?' says I.

'Aye min, we're jist rare, bit fit aboot you? We hinna seen ye for months, an we wis jist thinking like; we ken ye've hid a bad time o't but it's aboot time ye saw something apairt fae the fower wa's o' this hoose. So, come on min, pit yer jaiket on and we'll go oot for dram.'

They were richt of course. Efter the death o' my wife, lost far too soon at jist twenty-six years aul, I didna wint tae see onybody. I moped aboot the hoose for a few months, an' it

46

jist seemed easier nae tae see fowk at a'. I still hidna gotten ower it but the pain and loss werrna sae sherp as afore. I kent they were richt, an thocht a couple o' oors awa fae the hoose widnae dae ony herm.

'Come in boys an gie's a minute or twa tae get ready,' I said.

I'd had a shave and a shower earlier on, so it wis jist a case o' pittin on anither sark and gie'n mysel a squirt wi deodorant. Within minutes I wis back doon the stair and ready tae go.

We heidid for the city centre, an I kent it micht be hard kind, gaen tae some o' the places I used tae go wi her, bit it hid tae be faced some time I telt mysel. We started aff wi some o' the places on Justice Mill Lane – the local paper is inclined tae dub it 'Sunset Strip' because o' a the pubs and clubs. We wint in tae a few, fair hoachin wi fowk, an hid a couple o' drinks. During the next twa oors we made oor wye alang the street until we found oorsel's on Windmill Brae, very like Justice Mill Lane, wi lots o' clubs and pubs.

There wis a fair crowd o' fowk gaen aboot, young fowk, lassies and lads mingling and standin, smoking ootside the doors and on the pavements. Club 'bouncers,' wi radio heidsets, dressed in black, twa 'strippers' ootside Buggsy Broon's wearing jaikets and nithin much else by the look o't, ha'en a smoke. A busy nicht in the toon.

My hert went aff like an alarm clock and my stomach

fair lurched. There, in amang a crowd o' fowk jist coming roon the corner fae Bath Street, wis a familiar dear face. I lookit awa an telt mysel I wis daft, it wis jist somebody that lookit like her. I hardly dared look again bit I forced mysel tae dae it. The crowd had thinned oot a bit and noo I could see better. I could hardly get breath – it *wis* her, an as I lookit she smiled a hert stopping smile, sae sad and sweet that I felt the tears come tae my een. She smiled again and waved tae me. I stood there, rooted tae the spot, and she beckoned tae me, smilin a the while.

'Are ye a' richt min?' ane o' my pals said, 'Ye're nae looking affa great.'

'Nah, I'm nae feelin great at a,' I replied. 'Look, I dinna wint tae spile yer nicht, I've enjoyed mysel boys, it wis good o' ye tae tak me oot, bit I'm nae feelin great, so I'll heid for hame if it's a the same tae you?'

So, efter handshakes a roon, and a promise tae meet up the week efter, I teen aff across the street tae try and solve the mystery, bit by the time I crossed the cobblestone paved road she wis halfwye up the brae. I lookit at her retreatin figure, an jist then she turned tae me as if tae say, 'Come on then,' syne walked on. I hurried tae catch up bit she turned intae a club wi used tae go tae in happier times and wis gone! I'd lost her, and I thocht I'd niver find her in a this steer bit I slowly scanned the crowd an at last saw her standin roon the ither side o' the dance flee'r.

48

She smiled and waved again.

She wis affa elusive. Every time I thocht I wis getting closer, she seemed farrer awa.

'Weel, fit dae ye expect,' I thocht tae mysel. 'She's nae real – yer probably hallucinatin, or gaen aff yer heid.'

I struggled tae get through the packed crowd, bit finally managed tae get within aboot twenty or thirty feet o' her, as she turned aff the main room intae a 'quiet' bar. I saw her standing behind a lovely, tall lassie and as I approached, she smiled ae last time, touched the lassie's airm, and disappeared.

The lassie behaved as is if she'd been electrocuted. She shuddert quite violently at the ghostly touch, and lookit roon tae see if onybody hid noticed. Nae doot I was standin there wi my mou open at the turn o' events. She smiled at me, syne laughed.

'Somebody jist walked across my grave,' she said explaining hersel.

If only she kent the truth I thocht tae mysel.

Weel, tae cut a lang story short, I got spikin tae the lassie. We hid a few drinkies, and got on like a hoose on fire. She wis affa easy tae speak tae, an affa good company, an I forgot my troubles an woe's for a few oors. Come closing time I offered tae tak her hame an tae my surprise she agreed. Ower the next few weeks we saw each ither a fair bit. In anither few months we moved in thegither and eventually

49

got merried. I never thocht I'd find anither wife, an I wisnae even lookin, bit there ye go. That's the wye it happens sometimes.

Sometimes, fin I'm on my ain, maybe late at nicht, I think o' whit happened. I've niver believed in ghosts but whit happened that nicht wis hard, in fact impossible tae deny. So I dinna try, I just thank my first wife. I've still got, an will aye hae, a special place in my hert for her. I can niver forget her an the love that brocht her back tae me for a wee whiley. She played the pairt o' "go-between," tae perfection, bringing my new wife and me thegither, and I thank her wi a my hert. Aye, life can be gye queer sometimes.

6. THE HAUNTED HOTEL

This story is true, and actually happened to my brother and myself. When it comes to ghosts or paranormal events I've always had an open mind, neither believing nor disbelieving. I remain to be convinced, although the following events seemed real enough at the time. I heard 'something' but never saw what, or who it was. I'll leave it to you to make up your own mind.

In the summer of 1976 - or it may have been 1977 - I'm not quite sure of the actual date all these years later, I was 'on tour,' with a band. One of our dates was in Nairn, a small northern coastal town not far from Inverness. We'd played there before but always on the return leg of a tour, which meant we had never stayed overnight in the town, always preferring to drive home the eighty or so miles after the performance. However, on this occasion we had taken a booking on the outward leg of the tour and consequently booked into a local hotel.

Having arrived in the town in the early afternoon we set up our amplifiers, drums and P.A. system in the hall of the venue. We ran through a few songs just to check that everything was working properly and even rehearsed a few bits and pieces as bands often do when on the road. Satisfied that everything was in fine working order, we made our way to the hotel, which had been booked for us by the organisers of the venue. It was a lovely summer afternoon and we soon found the hotel, which was just off the main street on a road leading to the harbour and beach. It was a substantial old granite building; a proper hotel, not a bed and breakfast, and we were shown to our room on the first floor. As it turned out all the accommodation was in one very large room, what in a more modern hotel would be given the fancy title of a family room. There were two single beds and a double, so my brother and I took the double, giving the other two band members the singles.

The band played well that night and it was a great crowd. We always got a good reception at that particular club, and having played there before, we knew a lot of people who came up after the show and spoke to us. It was getting quite late but amongst the audience were a few musicians we knew well, who invited us back to their house for a small party. Not wanting to appear unsociable or offend anyone, we agreed to go back with them for an hour or so. It's easy to get a reputation for being 'big-headed' or worse when you're a musician with a professional touring band, so sometimes it's just easier to 'go with the flow.' It's really lovely when people like you enough to want to be in your company and offer you their hospitality, and we were always very grateful for that.

By the time we'd done socialising; singing a few songs and generally having a good time, it was getting very late indeed, so being a small town, the hotel wasn't too far away and we walked back the short distance to it. It was a beautiful summer night, late June, or early July, and the weather was very mild.

My brother and I don't drink - no particular reason why - we're definitely not religious or anything, we just don't drink alcohol, but the other two band members were a bit the worse for wear. They 'walked' down the road, hanging on to each other, singing an old Jacobite song, of which, 'Bonnie Charlie's No Awa,' was the only line they seemed to know, which was understandable since it wasn't in our repertoire.

As we got closer to the hotel we managed to quieten them down a bit, because we didn't want their singing to waken any of the other residents. Finally, we got them somewhat noisily upstairs and into the room, where they both threw themselves down on top of their beds, fully dressed, and immediately fell asleep.

My brother left the room to go to the toilet, there being no such thing as ensuite facilities in those days. I sat on the edge of the bed waiting for him to come back as I wanted to go too. He came back pretty quickly and I asked him where the toilet was. He told me it was down at the end of the corridor. I went out, closing the door behind me but it was really dark at this end of the corridor and I groped along the walls searching for a light switch with no success. I stopped for a moment to let my eyes adjust to the lack of light, but as

I stood there, I heard the floorboards creaking at the far end of the corridor, although I couldn't see anything. Thinking it may have been the hotelier disturbed by our less than discrete entry, I decided that discretion was the better part of valour and retreated back into the room.

'You're back affa quick,' was my brother's comment as I came back in and closed the door.

'Aye it was too dark, I couldnae find the light switch, and there's somebody moving aboot doon at the far end o' the corridor. I'm nay that desperate, I'll haud it in,' I joked.

'There's something at the end o' the corridor right enough,' said my brother, 'I've just seen it.'

There was a moment of silence as I digested this information.

'How d'ye mean, *it*?' I enquired.

'Jist what I said, "it," it's nae a person, or onything I've ever seen before,' he said, and this is what he told me.

'I went oot ontae the steps. (There were two steps leading down from our room to the corridor). I looked for the light switch jist like you, but couldnae find it, so I edged my wye along the corridor in the dark. It's nae sae dark doon at the far end because there's a great big windae in the ceiling, stained glass kind o' affair. The moonlight wis shining through and it wis quite clear. I heard somebody walking back and fore and thought maybe the manager or somebody wis up and aboot, disturbed because o' the noise the two boys

54

made coming in. I was a' ready wi my excuses and apologies, but then I saw something, jist beyond the moonlight, at the far side, in the darkness. It was jist moving back and fore, side tae side. It had nae human or animal shape. The nearest I can describe it was that it was aboot the size o' your Marshall speaker cabinet, (Approx 36"x36") nae very tall, broad and squat, jist moving back and fore. The hairs on the back o' my neck and airms stood on end, I couldnae stop watching it, kinda mesmerised by it. I managed tae tak my eyes aff it, maybe somebody in one o' the ither rooms coughed, or made some sort o' noise and broke the spell, and I backed doon the corridor and back intae the room,' he finished.

We sat there for a minute or two saying nothing, but by now it was about three in the morning and we were exhausted. He was already in bed, so I undressed and got into bed too. As we lay there we could hear the creaking from the far end of the corridor.

'Is it my imagination, or is that creaking getting closer?' I asked, seeking confirmation of my fears, and for once hoping I was wrong.

'Aye, it sounds closer to me, it's louder onywye,' said my brother.

In the next half hour, the creaking got louder and louder until it seemed to be right outside our door, and there it stayed for the rest of the night. Backwards and forwards, backwards and forwards it went, the creaking floorboards announcing its unwelcome presence. The sound would stop from time to time, and just when we were beginning to hope it had gone, it started again.

I had visions of the 'thing,' bursting open the unlocked door and some unspeakable horror coming into the room. The thought was almost as bad as the actuality, but no such thing happened. The evil, whatever it was, stayed outside the door. I remember saying to my brother at one point that we would know if it was something evil, because evil doesn't like the light and, being close to midsummer, the dawn would soon be with us. My words were quite prophetic, for as it got lighter the sounds outside the door lessened until with daylight they stopped entirely. We finally managed to fall asleep about 5am.

Hotels don't make any allowances in the morning for sleepless nights, no matter what time you manage to fall asleep and when someone knocked at our door about 8am announcing that breakfast was being served we duly got up, washed and trooped down to the dining room. Sitting at the table one of the now sober band members said he'd had a great sleep and asked if we had slept well. When we told him what kind of night we'd had he thought we were joking and laughed. We finally convinced him we were telling the truth and it wasn't a joke, but he still laughed. He thought it all highly amusing, and when the hotel proprietor came into the

56

dining room, he could hardly wait to tell him of our disturbed night, thinking the hotel owner would deny it and say it was all nonsense. Instead the hotel owner confirmed our story.

'Well, they won't be the first to say they heard something strange up there,' was all he said.

Our friend wasn't quite so cocky now after hearing that and packed first thing after breakfast. He couldn't wait to get out of the place.

There was no other confirmation of the story, no follow up to tie it all up nicely in a neat package. We never went back there and we heard nothing more about it. Of course, if we had been really brave, or insatiably curious, we could always have opened the door to confront whatever was out there and get to the bottom of it, to find out the truth. Just ask yourself – would you have opened that door?

7. THE IMPUDENT WEE SNOTTER

This event took place many years ago – in that period before the Second World War, when everyone was a bit more innocent, and life was lived at a more leisurely pace. Not that making a living wasn't a struggle; in fact it was even harder then. There was no welfare state and no national health service – a time when it was seen as a shameful thing to be in receipt of money from the "Parish" to sustain life and limb.

My grandfather and grandmother lived on the Shooting Hill, not far from Strachan, on Deeside, and brought up a big family in conditions which must have been overcrowded to say the least. My grandfather called himself a "general dealer", which meant he bought and sold just about anything that would turn a profit. He never learned to read or write, which wasn't uncommon for someone born in the 1880's, but he could count just fine when it came to money. He was a very astute and clever businessman and by the early 1950's had bought two farms on the outskirts of Banchory.

However, as I said, this story took place in the 1930's. One of the things my grandfather used to buy as a general dealer was rabbit skins. The more squeamish among you might think that was horrible or gruesome but that's just a sign of how divorced we've become from real life in our modern, sanitised, supermarket, way of living. Just about any countrywoman worth her salt could skin and gut a rabbit with ease. Hens for instance didn't come nicely packaged and cleaned in a plastic bag. You had to catch it first, thraw its neck, hang it for a few days by the feet, and then pluck the feathers by hand, gut it and cook it. They were called hens, but that was before the marketing folk got their hooks into the language and changed it to chickens. Real chickens are small and fluffy, about the size of sparrows.

Getting back to rabbits, although they are more likely to be pets than food these days, up until the 1950's they were an important source of meat for country folk. One of the by products of eating rabbits was the skins. Rabbit skins were used in the fur trade but the fur is also used in the manufacture of felt for making hats, etc.

Part of my grandfather's income came from the buying and selling of rabbit skins. His "beat" was all of Deeside - from Banchory up to Braemar - and sometimes beyond into Glenshee. He knew all the gamekeepers on all the great estates on Deeside; Invercauld, Glentanar, and Balmoral included; and would visit them on a regular basis. He visited the farmers too, for they shot rabbits as well, not only for the pot but to stop them destroying their crops.

One of the estates he visited regularly was Balmoral, which belonged to the royal family. Every year they would come up to Scotland on holiday, and stay at their castle on

59

Deeside. To my grandfather, it was just like any other estate. He went about his business, haggled with the keepers over the latest price for skins and left. One day while on his way to visit one of the more remote cottages, on a narrow back road, he encountered a car coming in the opposite direction.

My grandfather was driving a horse and cart, which made it next to impossible to reverse without ending up in a ditch or suchlike. The driver of the car was not amused and made his displeasure obvious, when he had to reverse a fair distance back to a place where the car and cart could pass. However, as my grandfather's cart drew close to the passing place, the driver got out and was very abusive. They had no right being there he asserted, etc, etc. Adding a few choice swear words for emphasis.

'Aye, he wis a toff gadgie, an' maist toff hantle are a' richt. Weel mannert folk, bit this hoolit wis jeest a richt nesty wee mannie,' my granny told me.

My grandfather said nothing but my granny, from her superior position on the cart, looked down on the blustering, bad tempered 'gentleman' and with all the scorn she could muster, she uttered the immortal rebuke.

'Wha dae you think yer speaking tae, ye impudent wee snotter? Dinna speak tae me like that, or I'll dicht yer chin withoot a hankie.'

At that point, my grandfather g-eed on the horse and they left the bemused man, still standing in the road.

'Oh Jeannie, Jeannie', he groaned further up the road, 'yer gaun tae get us the jile. That gadgie ye were gien a' the lip tae wis the king, and ye jist cried him an impudent wee snotter.'

'I wisnae caring,' my granny told me, a good thirty years after the event. 'He wisnae a richt king onywye. It wis thon Edward the Eighth.'

Her voice dripping with scorn, she dismissed him completely by circling her finger round and round beside her temple adding, 'Aye, thon Edward, the bammy king.'

8. THE MAN THAT NEVER GREW AULD

There was once a man who came and went; where he came from nobody knew, where he went to, nobody knew. He was a tall, dark haired man whom women found attractive and personable, and men found a pleasant companion. He could hold his own in intellectual conversation, or dispense a rough joke with ease round the barroom table. He was all things to all men, but to women he was a heartbreaker.

He never stayed in one place for long, preferring to take short-term work on the farms and factories, occasionally staying a few years, but on the whole he preferred to move on after a few months, or a year at most. He rarely returned to a place he'd been employed or an area where he'd lived. He had many acquaintances but no friends, for he allowed no person the intimacy that true friendship required. Only the women he knew loved him, and without exception he left them all, to wonder where he had gone and why.

In the spring of 1894 he found himself employed on a farm in the north east of Scotland. He was an experienced farm worker and the short-term nature of the work suited him fine. Typically, he would sign on for a six monthly fee and move on at the end of the 'term' but occasionally stayed longer if he found the work interesting and the people agreeable. The people he found most agreeable were young women, for he liked their company and companionship but paradoxically it was their ability to get beyond his facade and defences that invariably caused him to leave. He was not a heartless seducer; on the contrary, he loved women and cared deeply for those he became involved with, but sooner or later he knew he would have to leave them. He reasoned to himself that "sooner" was best for their benefit, no matter how much he loved them, for it gave them the chance to build a new life without him while they were still young. He had looked back with regret many times, as he was leaving, with tears in his eyes.

The farm he found himself on that spring of 1894 was a large one; the farmer was pleasant enough and best of all he had a beautiful daughter. She was an intelligent, dark haired girl, twenty one years old, of middling height, slim, but not skinny, with a ready smile and dark eyes that could steal any man's heart. Her name was Elizabeth, but she was known as Lizzie to all who knew, or met her.

He knew Lizzie was different from the very start and after a few months he knew he loved her like no other woman he'd ever met. Spring turned to autumn, and then to spring again, and still he stayed. When she told him that she was going to have his bairn they made hasty arrangements and were married within a month or so. He told himself he was a fool and that it would only lead to eventual heartbreak but he felt powerless to stop himself. He knew he was weak when it came to loving Lizzie but he was tired of moving on and told himself, just a little happiness, and he would be on his way soon. But a year passed, then another. A son was born, then a beautiful daughter, which only made any plans he had for leaving more difficult, for how could a man fail to love his children? Now he was thrice tied, and his love for Lizzie and his children only grew with time.

All too soon, ten years had passed and he had built a comfortable life for himself and his growing family, for now he had another son, another daughter. Lizzie bloomed in motherhood and was more beautiful than ever in his eyes, but all along, grumbling in the background, was his guilt and regret at what he must inevitably do. Still, he told himself 'a few more years,' two or three at the most before he slipped off into the night. And in this way yet another ten years passed.

Occasionally Lizzie would joke about how he never seemed to change, and told him she was glad of it, for she loved and adored him. But it was becoming noticeable, it seemed to him, that Lizzie grew naturally older with the years, while he remained the same. Other folk, family and neighbours were noticing too and sometimes they made small jokes about his never changing appearance. He brushed them off with a good-natured joke and a laugh but inside he worried that his time here was almost gone.

Everything came to a head soon after Lizzie's forty-second birthday. By sheer chance an old tinker woman came to the door one day, selling her wares and offering to tell fortunes. Lizzie invited her in and offered the old woman some tea and cake, which she gratefully accepted. Lizzie bought some things from the old lady, needles, two or three pirns of thread, and some elastic, and then allowed the woman to read her fortune.

'Oh missus, god bless ye, but there's a dark cloud hings ower yer life an family. I dinna like tae tell fowk bad things, bit there it is, a canna mak a better o' it,' she warned. 'I'm richt sorry, an efter you being sae kind tae me as weel.'

Lizzie felt herself go cold with fear. She didn't believe in fortune telling and such like and had only let the woman tell her fortune to be charitable; but the matter of fact, earnest way the old woman spoke somehow filled her with dread.

'Are you sure?' Lizzie asked.

'Aye, it's there, nae doot, a big dark cloud, it's been wi ye for mony's a year. It will lift soon, but it trails misery an sorrow ahin it. Be careful lassie, be careful,' she said with regret in her voice.

As she turned to go, the old woman happened to look at the photos Lizzie had displayed on the sideboard. A family group of her husband, herself and the children.

'This is yer femily lassie?' she announced as much as asked.

'Aye, my man, and bairns,' Lizzie said proudly.

Picking up the framed photograph, the old woman studied it closely. White faced she turned to Lizzie.

'If it wisnae impossible, I'd say that wis my man standin there lassie. He's the spit o' my Jimmy,' the old woman said, her voice trembling with emotion.

'Really?' said Lizzie, thinking the old woman was havering, 'but how old would your husband be now?'

'Seventy six, or seventy seven, I forget. It's been sae lang since I seen him.'

Tears welled up in the old woman's eyes and she wiped them away with the back of her hand.

'What happened tae him?' Lizzie asked, thinking he must be dead.

'Tae tell the truth, naebody kens,' she replied. 'He jist vanished ae day, an we never heard fae him again. Efter twa happy years, he disappeared, leavin me broken hairted. I thocht he must be deid, drooned maybe, or the Burkers got him, or been in an accident or sic like, bit I never saw his face again 'til this minute. Yer man's the very image o' him, I sweer tae God lassie.'

'Well, my man's name is James as weel, but it's nae possible for them tae be the same man noo, is it?' asserted Lizzie. 'My man's in his forties, an your man wid be in his seventies. Maybe their related or something,' she finished lamely.

'I'll tell ye whit lassie,' said the old woman, 'I hae a

photy o' my man, an I'll come back the morn an let ye see it. Ye'll see for yersel, they're like twa peas in a pod.'

The old woman took her leave, leaving Lizzie to ponder the mystery until her husband came home.

'James,' she said later that night after the supper dishes were cleared away and washed. 'The queerest thing happened the day.'

'Aye,' he asked, reading the newspaper, 'fit wis 'at like?'

'Weel, there wis an auld tinker wifie came roon the doors this efterneen. I askit her in, and bocht a few bitties fae her jist tae be charitable like.'

'Fit's queer aboot 'at?' James asked.

'She read my fortune an said there wis a big black cloud hingin ower oor femily an oor happiness. It gave me a bit o' a fear, I hiv tae admit,' said Lizzie.

'Ach! Fortune telling, it's a' nonsense,' he said scornfully.

'Maybe, bit 'at wisnae the queerest bit. She saw yer photy on the sideboard and said you were her man. Fit dae ye think o' that?' she asked.

There was a silence for a few minutes – James seemed dumbstruck, speechless, eventually coughing and getting up out of his chair. He went over to the photo on the sideboard and picked it up, looking at it silently for a few moments.

'She must be daft, nae richt in the heid,' he

67

eventually got out. 'How could I be her man; an aul woman o' her age?'

'Well, she's comin back the morn wi a photy o' him tae let me see. It should be interesting tae see foo much like ye he really is – fit dae ye think?'

'Aye, interesting richt enough,' he said quietly.

Next morning James rose early as usual and after breakfast announced he had to go into the village for some errands. He kissed Lizzie as he left, mounted the horse and rode out through the yard gate, looking back and waving to her. She would relive that moment again, and again, and again, in her memory, for that was the last time she ever saw him.

The old woman came back that day and they compared the photos, side by side. If Lizzie didn't know it was impossible she would have sworn they were the same man. They had the same hair, the same eyes and mouth, the same face; to all intents and purposes it was the same man. When Lizzie agreed with the old woman about the resemblance, the woman crossed herself.

'God bless us lassie, he's nae natural. I dinna ken fit he is, bit it's nae richt,' she said with fear in her voice.

'Oh!" said Lizzie, trying to find some rational explanation, 'he canna be the same man, for he hisnae aged ony,' and as she said it, she remembered all the little jokes they'd shared about him never changing and still looking the same.

She felt as if she'd been hit by a train. Her brain raced to find some reason, as she broke out in a cold sweat and she gasped for breath. She sat down and, putting her hands over her face, cried as if her heart would burst.

'I'll leave noo lassie,' the tinker woman said quietly, 'I'm sorry tae hae brocht ye sae muckle grief.'

She let herself out and left. James didn't return, and Lizzie got no sleep that night. She cycled into the village next day and asked if anybody had seen him but there was no sign of him. She reported him missing to the village bobby and returned home. When Lizzie went to look for the old woman, the tinker encampment was deserted. They'd moved on and were gone, leaving only the cold grey ashes of the campfire and wizzened grass where the tents had been.

Lizzie, although frantic with worry, knew within her heart that she would never see him again. Inquiries later found that he had caught the train from the village station into Aberdeen and from there he vanished without a trace. Many months later a telegram arrived from the war department regretting that her husband, James Henderson, was reported missing, believed killed in action on the western front, for the year was 1916, and the First World War raging. Almost a year later a parcel with his personal belongings arrived, including his army pay-book. He was listed as Private James Henderson, aged 27. There was a letter addressed to her amongst the pitiful remains of his life.

'My Darling Lizzie, I loved you like no other. I should have left many years ago, but in my selfishness and love for you, I stayed too long, please try to forgive me. Kiss the bairns for me.

I'm sorry lass, so very, very sorry – James.'

Lizzie never remarried and never stopped mourning her James. She often wondered if he had truly died in France, or if he had taken advantage of the insane mayhem of the trenches to disappear and switch identities. She liked to think he was still out there somewhere, still handsome and forever young.

9. MRS MCFARLANE

Many years ago, my wife and I were invited to attend a wedding in Alloa, near Stirling. We decided to book into a local hotel the night before the wedding and thus avoid driving the hundred or so miles on the big day. It was a small, family run hotel not far from Stirling, quiet and secluded, but with a restaurant open to the public. My wife and I had almost finished the main course of our evening meal when three ladies entered the restaurant and sat at a table about ten feet away. The restaurant wasn't busy, and despite the taped background music, any conversation was easily overheard. Two of the ladies were in their late fifties and could only be described as, 'matronly,' while the other lady was very old and frail and sat between the two. We never found out the names of the matronly pair but they addressed the old lady, loudly and frequently, as 'Mrs McFarlane.'

It soon became obvious that Mrs McFarlane was deaf, or as we preferred to believe afterwards, just as deaf as she wanted to be. The matrons talked to each other in loud Morningside accents and spoke *at* the old lady rather than to her. Then they would speak to each other about Mrs McFarlane as if she weren't there.

'Poor dear, she can't hear a thing these days,' said one, which was all too obviously addressed to the room rather than her friend.

'Yes, it's such a shame,' her companion replied with just as much sincerity, 'it's a terrible affliction to be deaf.'

Quite unexpectedly, Mrs McFarlane passed wind. Only the expression, 'loud and proud,' could do justice to her efforts. There was no chance of pretending it was a squeaky chair, or any other such feeble excuse. This was a fart with a capital, 'F.' While the two matrons turned all shades of red with embarrassment, Mrs McFarlane chewed stoically on, seemingly oblivious to their discomfiture, or her unwitting comment on their conversation.

'Aye, I bet you're wishing *you* were deaf and hadn't heard that beauty,' I thought, trying hard not to laugh out loud.

'Oh my, Mrs McFarlane, are you all right?' one asked, trying to gloss over the incident, but making sure at the same time that everybody in the room knew she wasn't the culprit.

Mrs McFarlane nodded and smiled, but didn't answer, reminding me instantly of Mr Wemmik's exhortation to Pip in Great Expectations, '*Nod and smile to aged P.*'

After much fussing around and talking at Mrs McFarlane, things appeared to settle back to normal, but I swear to this day that she was merely drawing them in, lulling them into a false sense of security. She struck without warning, cutting incisively through the conversation with another ripper, which would have done credit to a revving Harley Davidson motorbike.

'Oooh! Mrs McFarlane,' exclaimed the first matron, waving her hand in front of her face in a fanning motion.

I had the sudden thought that, if twentieth century ladies were as susceptible to 'swooning,' as women of the eighteenth and nineteenth century, then the discomfited matron would have fainted clean away. Luckily my wife and I seemed to be upwind of Mrs McFarlane's aromatic efforts, unlike the unfortunate twosome sharing her table.

'Poor dear, she can't control herself these days,' explained the second matron to her friend, and more importantly, the dining room.

Matron number one didn't reply, but seemed to be holding her breath so as not to inhale, which only succeeded in turning her face the same colour as her bouffant blue rinse.

Just like Mrs McFarlane, we couldn't hold it back any longer and we laughed out loud. My wife dissolved into fits of giggles, closely followed by myself. The matrons glared at us, but the few other patrons of the restaurant were laughing too. We had finished our meal by this time and were waiting for coffee but decided to beat a retreat and have our coffee taken to the residents lounge. As we stood up to leave, still laughing, I looked over at Mrs McFarlane, who smiled, and very deliberately winked at me.

10. THE QUEEN O' SWANS

In Scottish folklore there are many tales of shape changing beings. Unfortunately, their interactions with the human race mostly end with dire consequences for the humans. I'm thinking primarily of the Great Selkie, and the numerous tales of water kelpies, and no doubt there are even more I'm not, as yet, aware of. When I was thinking up a story to base a song on, I invented the Queen O' Swans, which is altogether a much gentler and romantic encounter with the supernatural world.

The resulting song, 'Walker Dam,' is one of my most popular songs, which I set on Walker Dam, an old industrial dam in the West end of Aberdeen. Its original purpose long redundant, it's now a favourite beauty spot, populated by ducks, geese and swans, in the leafy suburb of Craigiebuckler. This story is based on the song.

* * *

Jack Wyness was a lonely man. His mother had died when he was just twelve years old and his father, who had brought him up single handedly, had recently died too. At the age of 34 he was alone in the world, with no family apart from a few cousins scattered the length and breadth of the British Isles, some even further afield. Jack was not a 'loner' by inclination, having many friends at school and University and was not averse to the occasional night out with the boys. But as he'd grown older these became less frequent, as the friends married or moved away and lost touch. For the last few years his father's illness meant even less time for Jack to socialise and so he accidentally fell into being a 'loner' rather than seeking it out. As for women, well he'd had his share and his moments, let there be no doubt about that; but he'd never found that one person, the soul mate that all the literature speaks about.

It fell about the middle of July late in the evening when Jack, who had been busy all day, decided to go for a late night stroll by the banks of Walker Dam. He'd come home from work, cooked himself something to eat and promptly fallen asleep in an armchair. When he woke a few hours later his muscles ached and his back felt stiff and sore.

Late as the hour was he left the house for a short walk to clear his head and get some fresh air. It was a pleasant summer evening, still light to the north, where just a few hundred miles away the midnight sun held sway. Still warm and mild from the remains of the heat built up during the day, there was a gentle, playful breeze whispering through the trees as he made his way round the edge of the dam.

Despite the lateness of the hour, it was still not completely dark, for in these northern latitudes the summer days are long, the nights short, and dawn comes early. There is a good old-fashioned Scottish word for that particular

75

quality of light between sunset and full darkness and that word is, 'gloamin.' So, it was in the gloamin that Jack found himself by the shores of Walker Dam. He was entirely alone, no one else here at this hour; all was silent apart from the occasional quack of ducks, or rustling of some bird or animal in the long grass at the water's edge.

Quite unexpectedly, he became aware of a figure standing on the bank ahead, between the water and the footpath. At first it just looked like a white shape, too hard to distinguish in the failing light, but as he drew closer he realised that it was a woman, then closer still and it became not just a woman but a beautiful young woman, dressed entirely in white. As he drew level with her she smiled at him but said nothing, and for his part he shyly acknowledged her presence, nodding and wishing her a quiet, 'Good evening,' as he passed her by.

He wondered what a young woman was doing out here on her own so late at night and was still trying to work it out when he realised she was behind him on the footpath, following him. He reassured himself she was just going in the same direction and not to be so paranoid, but she quickly caught up and took his hand. Startled by this, he stopped dead in his tracks and looked at her, but again she said nothing, just smiled a radiant smile that lit up her already beautiful face.

'I'm sorry lass, I dinna ken wha ye are. Ye must be

mistakin' me for somebody else,' he said, his heart racing with the unexpectedness of the encounter. Now that he was face to face with her he could see that her dress was made of a muslin type fabric, with white feathers somehow interwoven into the fabric. It left very little to the imagination, almost transparent in places, revealing; yet concealing her slim, delicate figure. Her face was pale, skin like fine translucent egg-shell porcelain, clean straight features, with dark eyes that were up-tilted giving her a strange and exotic look. Her long hair was the whitest he'd ever seen, and looking down he saw that she wore no shoes; her feet were bare, small and dainty. He thought she looked about twenty-three or twenty-four years old, but it was hard to tell, and when she spoke at last, her voice soft and sibilant, husky, made him hang on her every word.

'Oh, thou art the very man I'm looking for,' she confirmed, 'and many times I've watched thee feed the swans. I know thee well, for I've watched thee almost every day for months, coming here to feed the birds. It seems to me that thou have a great love for the swans,' she declared.

'Aye, I love swans, they're the bonniest, and noblest o' a' the birds in my opinion. I love tae see them swimming here and there upon the water.'

'I knew it, thou have a good heart, filled with kindness, and tonight sir, your kindness will be repaid, here on the banks of Walker Dam,' she promised.

Taking his arm, she led him off the path, into the more heavily wooded part of the shoreline. Luckily, the moon was now high in the sky, and with the summer night being so light, it was quite easy for him to pick his way among the trees. She seemed to know where she was going, so he allowed himself to be led deeper into the wood. At the back of his mind a wee voice was telling him that he was a fool to go with this strange woman, but another stronger urge told him to take a chance, see where she might lead. For all he knew he might be attacked and robbed by some waiting accomplice at any moment, but at last she stopped and turned to him. He looked about him and could see by the light of the moon that they were in a small sheltered clearing where the bushes and shrubs grew very densely together. The word, 'bower,' popped into his mind as he remembered the fairy stories his dear mother used to read to him when he was young. There was an arrangement of sorts on the ground made from thin branches and foliage, with a layer of ferns and moss on top but before he had any time to speculate on its purpose she turned and drawing him close to her, spoke quietly.

'Thou must be wondering who I am, and why I have brought thee to this place?' she said.

'Aye, indeed I am, for its nae every day that I meet a beautiful young woman, wha drags me into the bushes,' he joked, trying to make light of a very strange situation.

'Sir, I have been watching thee and the gentleness of thy manner,' she said earnestly, 'not only to the swans, but the other creatures too. As I watched and listened to thy voice I sensed much loneliness and sorrow.'

'That's true, for I have been lonely at times, and I've had my fill of sorrow these last few months I must admit,' he conceded.

'Then sorrow no more. Believe me sir when I say I have deliberated long and hard over this. I do not bestow my favours lightly.' There was almost a warning note in her voice.

'Aye, I can well believe that,' he said, captivated by the beauty of her face; the tone and sincerity in her voice sending shivers up his spine.

'Good, for thou must understand this clearly. Thou, and no other are my chosen man. If thee agree, I shall be thy queen, and thou shall be the King of Swans this night,' she offered.

His heart raced with excitement.

'You mean...?' His voice trailed off, hardly believing what was implied in her words.

'I do. Now talk no more my love and kiss me,' and reaching up on tiptoe she pulled his face closer to hers.

Their lips met, his senses reeled from the warmth and passion of her kiss, and slowly they sank down upon the nest of boughs and ferns.

Jack had never known such all-consuming sensuality to emanate from a woman before. Her skin was the softest he had ever known, her passion almost frightening in its intensity. As Jack drank in her beauty under the soft moonlight he was sure he must be dreaming. Closing his eyes he let himself be swept away, immersed in her. The blood thundered in his veins filling his mind and senses with a sound like the wing beats of a great bird. He felt light and dizzy as if floating a great height above the world, and afterwards she whispered in his ear.

'Oh my love, I have chosen well,' she said. 'Now I am indeed thy queen, true unto death. Kiss me and love me once more before the morning light,' she implored and Jack needed no second bidding.

Jack woke much later to the sound of the dawn chorus as the myriad birds of the woods sang their greeting to the new day. He turned to embrace his new love but his heart filled with loss as he realised she was gone! Hurriedly dressing, he made his way through the woods calling for her, looking here and there, but there was no sign of his pale princess. He circled Walker Dam twice, three times, searching thoroughly for her but she was gone, he finally conceded to himself, heartbroken. He made his way home, and later called his employers, telling them he was not well, which was true. He went back to Walker Dam twice more that day, searching on the off chance that she might have returned, and again in the evening at the same time as he had gone there the night before, but there was nothing. She had disappeared, vanished without trace.

A few nights later, on the night of the full moon, Jack lay in bed sleeping. He slept soundly, for the pain and distress at the loss of his new love had kept him awake these last few nights, until finally exhausted, he'd fallen into a deep, deep sleep. Jack dreamed, and in his dream he saw his love. On the banks of Walker Dam a beautiful swan appeared, swimming gracefully to the shore where he stood watching, and as it drew closer and stepped ashore it somehow grew and stretched to become his lost love. He reached for her and she came into his arms, warm and soft, and spoke to him, her voice low but clear.

'Do not feel abandoned my love, I must leave thee for a while, but I am thine and shall always be, as long as thou love no other. If thou love me truly and are constant, then we shall meet and love again,' she explained.

She kissed him then with the same passion and fervour as she had done before and turning away looked back at him as she entered the water, turning into a beautiful swan once more as she swam off. Jack woke, confused, disorientated for a moment, trying to fathom what the dream meant. He gave up after a while but when he had a similar dream at the time of the next full moon, and again at the next, and again at the next, he began to think the unthinkable. He kept his thought to himself, but continued to walk by the banks of Walker Dam each day, feeding the swans and ducks as he had done since he was a child. One swan in particular seemed to have an affinity with him and would come out of the water and settle down on the grass beside him. He talked to her as if she were human, earning himself a reputation as a mild eccentric from the other people who walked on the banks of Walker Dam, but Jack did not care. He was happy at last.

Jack never married and when he died, at a ripe old age, his remaining relatives who were charged with the duty of clearing out his home and possessions wondered for a few short moments why he had so many photographs of swans. If they only had the eyes to see, they would have realised that they were all of the same swan.

11. THE RUNNING MAN

This is a story told to me many years ago about my Auntie L..., and my grandfather. I was told that she was just a lassie when it took place. I got the impression that she was about 15 or 16, so that would date the story to around 1923/4.

My grandfather, auld Davy Stewart was well acquainted with all the gamekeepers and farmers on Deeside. Some he got on with just fine, but purely on a working level, and with others he became quite good friends. One day he set out to visit a keeper he hadn't seen for a while, taking my auntie with him. The keeper lived up a remote and lonely glen and since they hadn't set out until just after lunchtime it was about mid-afternoon before they reached his cottage. The keeper was fine pleased to see them as he didn't get many visitors and lived alone.

'Come awa in Davy, I see ye've brocht ane o' yer lassies tae. Well quine, ye'll jist hae tae excuse the state o' the place, for I'm nae a great yin for the cleanin'.'

My auntie said nothing, but she told me it wis a 'clatty keer, a richt boorach.'

He offered her tea but she refused politely, saying she'd had tea just before she left home. Travellers wouldn't accept tea or food from just anyone; they set very strict hygiene standards as regards preparation of food, washing of dishes, and cooking. They might well be 'gasping' for a cup of tea but they would refuse if they thought the person offering the tea was 'clatty.'

'Ye'll hae a dram though, Davy?' he offered my grandfather.

'Oh aye, we'd be nane the waur,' replied auld Davy who was fond of his dram, and so the two cronies sat at the table with their glasses of whisky, passing on the latest news.

My grandfather eventually got round to asking the keeper if he had any rabbit skins to sell.

'Aye there's a fair puckle oot in the shed,' replied the keeper, and so they all went out to the shed to get the skins and strike a bargain.

The keeper wasn't a hard man to deal with and always accepted whatever my grandfather offered, but on this day he wasn't even worried about the money.

'Ye'll hae got yer pipes wi ye, Davy?' he asked eagerly.

'Oh, aye,' said my grandfather, knowing full well that the keeper had a love for the bagpipes.

'Weel, jist you come intae the hoose, gie's a few selections on the pipes, and the skins are yours. Never mind the money, an we'll hae anither dram or twa forbye.'

This was exactly what my grandad was hoping to hear.

'Awa oot tae the trap and bring in my pipes" he said to my aunt, 'and gie Jeanie-Meer a drink while yer at it.'

Jeanie-Meer was his horse, a grey mare which my grandfather was especially fond of. He often spoke of her years later when reminiscing about old times. So, she did as her father asked, first bringing in the pipes and then going back out to 'water' the horse.

As the horse snuffled and drank from the bucket she could hear the wail of the pipes from inside the cottage as my grandfather tuned up. He was a good piper by anyone's standards, but not the best of the Stewarts, for they all played the bagpipes to varying degrees. His father-in-law for instance, my great grandfather - auld Donald Stewart o' Crichie - had been Scottish champion and had won so many medals for piping that he couldn't wear them all on his chest, and took to pinning the others on the back of his tunic. You can see auld Donald's gravestone in Crichie (Stuartfield) cemetery with the figure of a piper carved into the stone.

The afternoon soon wore on and my aunt was getting anxious about the time, for they had a fair journey back home. The two men seemed oblivious to the time, as the whisky flowed and the pipes skirled, but she eventually spoke up.

'Da, we'll need tae think aboot getting hame, for it'll soon be dark,' she advised.

'Aye yer richt enough, it is getting a bittie late, weel then, I suppose we'll hiv tae go,' said my grandfather to his drinking crony, dismantling the ivory and silver mounted

85

pipes, and placing them carefully back in the box.

She took his pipes out to the trap and my grandfather loaded the rabbit skins, shaking hands with the keeper. Then they set out on the journey home.

About a mile and a bit further down the glen there was another keepers cottage at the road side and as they drew closer saw the keeper standing at his door, enjoying the last of the winter sun, smoking a clay pipe. He stepped out into the road and waved them down.

'Och, it yersel Davy – I some thocht it must be you fin I heard the soon o' the pipes waftin doon the glen - noo jist haud on a minute, I've got some skins here for ye,' he said.

By the time the skins were loaded and the bargain concluded it was almost dark, but soon they were on the road again and heading for home.

About half a mile further on there was an old abandoned quarry just off the roadside and as they approached it the mare began to blow and snort.

'Haud back Jeanie, haud back,' my grandfather commanded the horse, adding, 'whit's wrang wi ye?'

Something was bothering her and he was finding it hard to stop her bolting. As they passed the quarry my aunt happened to glance over and saw a tall man standing at the entrance watching them.

'Da,' she said. 'Did ye deek thon queer gadgie standin' in the quarry?'

'Nah, I didna, I wis too busy trying tae haud Jeanie back, fit did he look like?' he asked.

'Tall, affa tall, wi a white face, and a' dressed in black,' she replied, looking back again.

The tall man had left the quarry and was running down the road after the horse and trap.

'Da, da, I'm feart, that shan gadgie is rinnin efter us,' she said.

He looked back over his shoulder and seeing the tall pale man was gaining on them he allowed Jeanie to speed up as she wished.

'Come in aboot tae me, and hing ontae my airm,' he ordered, making sure he was between her and the pursuing man.

Looking back she could see the man getting closer and closer despite the speed of the horse, until at last he drew level with the trap. As she looked up at him he seemed to loom over them. Trying to rationalise something that wasn't rational, she thought he must be on a penny-farthing bike to appear so tall, keeping up with a galloping horse and to be travelling so much faster than any normal man could run.

She chanced a glance over the side of the trap to see if that was indeed the case and despite the rapidly failing light she could see that she was wrong. There was no penny-farthing, and horror of horrors; there were no legs either. She looked at the creature's face with its white, white skin, and where the eyes should have been there was nothing but two black holes. She screamed.

'Da, da, it something that's nae richt, it's nae a man,' she shouted.

'Aye dearie, I ken,' he replied grimly, giving Jeanie her head. Jeanie ran as if all the devils in hell were after her but still the strange unnatural creature ran on beside them, silent and menacing.

'He's trying tae scare Jeanie an' rin us aff the road, bit I winna let him,' my grandfather said, using all his skill and expertise to let Jeanie run free, yet stopping her from drifting towards the edge of the road and crashing ruin.

The minutes seemed like hours as the ghoul ran on beside them but almost as quickly as their ordeal had started, it came to an end. The creature veered off and, still running, disappeared into the trees. They let Jeanie run for a wee while longer. But the same instinct that had warned her of danger, now informed her that it was safe to slow down and resume her normal pace.

A few months later my grandfather was visiting the same keeper again and mentioned the bother they had on the way home.

'Weel, it's funny ye should speak aboot that. A few folk aboot here hiv said they seen something nae richt aside the quarry, bit I've never heard o' it leaving the quarry and chasing fowk.'

'Aye, weel it did, so I'll be awa fae here lang afore dark,' warned my grandad.

'Ye'll hae heard o' the Grey Man o' Ben Macdhui?' said the keeper. 'Weel, the fowk aboot here cry fit ye saw the Black Man o' Ben Macdhui,' the keeper informed him. 'Mind you, we're miles fae the mountain here, but it's jist a name folk use.'

They never found out any more details about the ghoul, or any story to explain what happened, but they never ventured into that glen so late in the day again, and always left well before the sun set.

12. THE TINKER'S KISS

Emily Strachan pottered about in her kitchen, doing one of the myriad chores that were the lot of a farmer's wife. Today had been a right 'scuttery,' sort of day, the kind of day where she'd done so much but had, on the surface, so little to show for it. And it was still only just after 11am, according to the time showing on the 'wag-at-the-wa' clock. Its pendulum, slowly wagging back and forth, gave it its name, and the slow, steady tick only served to add to the tedium of the morning. She was fed up; the farm was a lonely place at the best of times and today her mood seemed to pile frustration on frustration upon her.

About twenty minutes later she went out to feed some kitchen refuse to the hens; cold tatties and such like left over from last night's supper. As she returned to the house she noticed a man walking up the narrow track to the farm. A little frightened, for her husband had gone to the mart in Aberdeen, Emily retreated to the door of the farmhouse and watched his approach. She was alone on the farm and didn't see strangers very often, which made her very wary, and besides, she was a naturally shy person.

He was a tall man, dark of hair, with a weather beaten sun tan to show he spent most of his time outdoors. He walked loosely, his gait easy and confident, and he looked well muscled and lean. Emily guessed he was perhaps a little older than her, but not by much, perhaps about thirty three, or thirty four to her thirty one. He doffed his bonnet in a mark of respect as he came closer.

'Good day to you Missus,' he called, stopping at least ten feet from the door.

He understood that she was nervous, and had considerately stopped a distance away so as not to alarm her.

'Who are you, and whit dae you want?' she called out, her voice quivering, still distrustful of him.

'D'ye remember last hairst, the tinkers that helped bring in the crops? Weel, I was one of them. We camped ower in yer back field there. We caused ye nae trouble, and were awa as soon as the hairst was in.'

She nodded, remembering well the colourful folk who had worked hard by day in her husband's fields and had sung and played the bagpipes and the fiddle round their campfire in the evening.

'I'm jist by mysel this time, working my wye from farm tae farm, village tae village, seeing if ye want onny pots or pans mended, or onny kind of job done aroon the place that the fermer maybe hisnae the time nor patience to dae himsel?' he concluded.

She relaxed and opened the door a little, stepping over the threshold. He had no need to take note of her fine figure and lovely face. He had marked them well last year but it did no harm to take another look he thought, scrutinising her

91

again as she thought of any possible jobs to be done. She looked up then and caught him looking at her, and he gave her a big friendly smile. She blushed, but smiled automatically in return, her heart thumping for some inexplicable reason. He was good looking, no arguments about that, she thought him a big strapping, handsome chap.

'I hae some things that need fixed richt enough,' she admitted, 'but my man is nae at hame richt noo and there's nae money in the hoose to pey ye. Maybe if ye come back later, fit aboot the morn?' she suggested.

'Nah Missus, sorry, I'll nae be deein that,' he stated regretfully. 'I believe it's bad luck tae go back on yer ain fit steps, so I winna be back this wye for a few months but,' he offered, suggesting an alternative, 'perhaps if ye gied me a meal, something tae eat, I could dee the work in exchange, for I've had nithing tae eat since yesterday.'

He omitted to tell her about the plump, juicy rabbit he had caught and cooked over his open fire the night before. Travelling people, knowing the ways of the fields and woods rarely went hungry, but sometimes it was best to put on 'the poor mooth,' an often used traveller ploy. In this case he was hoping to provoke a sympathetic response by pleading hunger and hope she was as kind as she looked. To her, his suggestion sounded like a perfect solution, for she had plenty of provisions in the house.

'I'll dee the work here on the doorstep,' he offered, and

92

she agreed, disappearing into the house, emerging a few minutes later with a couple of pots that had seen better days, including an enamel pail with an unfortunate chip in the white enamel, and the underlying metal, grown holed and leaky.

He sat down upon the front step and set to work right away, his tools in a pack he carried on his back, and began to measure the pieces of metal he would need to patch the items, cutting patches to fit. As he cut and hammered, mending first one item then another, he could smell cooking emanating from the farmhouse. His stomach fair rumbled with hunger but he ignored it as best he could and carried on.

Emily came out to watch him for a while. 'I've put on some tatties, and I hae bacon and plenty of eggs,' she added, making conversation.

He looked up at her, his dark eyes making her heart beat faster.

'That sound great to me Missus, thank ye,' he said, looking back at his work.

His hands looked strong, but not hardened and calloused like her husband's she thought. There was an elegance to the way he handled his tools, a surety and economy of movement, a skill she'd never seen before. She liked the way his dark hair curled over his neck, longer than most of the local farm workers, who still favoured the, 'short back and sides,' they'd been given in the trenches of Flanders to alleviate the problems of lice.

'Were ye in France?' she suddenly asked, her thoughts flitting by association from one thing to the next, not quite knowing why she asked.

'Aye, the Black Watch,' he replied, 'but I'd rather nae speak aboot it if ye please?'

She had heard those same words from so many of the men who had returned from France. She'd heard that the horrors they had seen there was something they preferred not to think about, far less talk about. She suddenly felt ashamed for no reason she could think of.

'Of course, I'm sorry, I shouldnae have asked, please forgive me,' she apologised, feeling herself blush.

'Nae need tae apologise. I was een of the lucky yins; I got hame again, and in one bit,' he said, a tinge of sadness in his voice.

She felt there had been some great loss here, from the way he spoke.

'Ye lost somebody,' she said, and it wasn't a question.

He looked up at her again; those big brown eyes looked decidedly moist. Her heart turned over with pity.

'Twa brithers,' was all he said, and he quickly looked back to his work again.

His back seemed like a silent rebuke to her idle curiosity.

'Oh god, I'm sae affa sorry,' was all she could say, and

94

she turned to go back into the farmhouse.

As she prepared the food she thought of the sacrifice made by all the thousands of young men in the recent conflict. But in his case, now that she thought of it, the sacrifice seemed even greater. He was a member of a despised tinker clan. Let's make no bones about it, she thought, the tinkers were looked down upon, despised, treated like dirt and even hated by some of the settled population. Yet, when the call to arms had come, they had stood and fought shoulder to shoulder, making the ultimate sacrifice for their country. She felt a tear trickle down her cheek for his loss. A knock at the door roused her from her reverie, and she hurried to the door.

'That's me done,' he said. 'Hae a look to mak sure yer happy wi the work,' and he handed over the items, realising that she couldn't carry them all, and so offered to carry them in for her.

She agreed, leading the way into the farmhouse and through to the large warm kitchen at the back of the house. She pronounced herself delighted with his work and asked him to sit down at the big kitchen table while she finished cooking for him. The smell of the sizzling bacon made his mouth water and he watched as she tested and then poured the potatoes, brushing back a loose strand of her dark hair as she replaced the pot on the stove.

Within minutes he had a plate of food placed before

him that consisted of 5-6 rashers of thick cut bacon, two fried eggs and as much potatoes as he could possibly eat. She cut thick slabs of bread from a loaf and buttered them generously, placing them on a plate to one side of his main plate, with a jug of steaming hot tea to wash it down. She watched as he ate, not openly, but from the corners of her eyes, so as not to make him self-conscious or embarrassed. To her surprise, for someone who hadn't eaten since the day before, he didn't 'wolf' the food down. He ate as he worked, quietly and methodically, obviously enjoying his food, which she liked to see. After a while he managed to clear the plate and, pushing the plate away, he leaned back in his chair.

'Weel, whit can I say? That was lovely, very tasty, and ye didnae try to mak a fool of me in onny wye.'

She raised a quizzical eyebrow, so he continued. 'Some folk would have tried to gie me as little as possible so the "bargain" was loaded in their favour. They'd maybe feed me brose, porridge or sic like, for cheapness sake, but I've found ye kind, generous and open hairted Mrs Strachan, and I thank ye for it.

'Och I could never dee that,' Emily replied, 'an honest wage for an honest day's work. Ye gave yer side o' the bargain and I returned it in full measure. I'm gled ye enjoyed yer food, although it was nithing fancy.'

She thought for a moment. 'Would some folk really be sae mean as tae feed ye brose for yer work?' she asked.

'Oh aye, efter a', I'm just a, "tinkie," to them - they use me and then try to get the best oot o' the bargain to suit themsels. Sometimes a fermer's wife or housekeeper micht get me to dee a' the jobs she wints deen and syne she'll tell me she has nae money. Sometimes, if I complain, they threaten to report me to the police, or set the dogs on me, but maist of them aren't as bad as that'

'Really? That's terrible. What dae ye dee then?' she asked, curious again.

He thought for a while, as if not sure whether he should tell her or not, for he didn't want her to feel frightened or threatened in any way.

'Well, if they are reasonable, and dinna set the dogs on me, I gie them the choice, o' the Tinkers curse, or the Tinker's kiss, but only if they're good looking,' he said at last, a shy smile on his face.

'The Tinker's Curse, can ye really dee that, put a curse on somebody?' she asked, her natural curiosity coming to the fore again.

'Oh aye, it's easy done,' he said, matter of factly. 'A' ye have tae dee is hold up yer left hand as if stopping the traffic like the policemen dee in the big toons, and then utter yer curse, whilst pointing at them wi your richt hand and gie them the "evil eye" by glowering at the person yer cursing.'

'I widnae like ye tae dee that tae me,' she said with a shiver. 'It sounds affa scary, I'd be feart.'

'There's nae need for ye to be feart, I dinna think ye are in onny danger of me cursing ye lass. Yer a very nice and kind person, nae danger at a'.'

She topped up his jug of tea, and took some for herself, sitting down at the table with him for the first time.

'Dis it really work?' she asked fascinated, eager for distraction from her tedious chores.

'Oh aye, they never seem to be lucky again efter I curse them. Some folk have even begged me. I swear, they've gotten doon on their knees and offered tae pey me what they're due, aye, and far mair, if I'll only tak the money and jist lift the curse,' he explained, warming to his subject, knowing she was engrossed by his tale.

If the truth be told, he knew it was all rubbish but it was a proud tinker tradition to tell stories, and outrageous lies, to entertain each other round the campfires at night. He could see she was interested and entertained by his tales of cursing. In his mind it was another way of repaying her for her generosity.

'What dae you say, when you're cursing them I mean?' she said as she pushed for more.

'I jist tell them they'll never hae good luck from that day forth, that things will go badly for them in the coming years, and a few mair bits besides. Onnything that comes tae mind really, but I never tell them onny one definite thing, such as, "yer broon coo will drap deid at twa o'clock next

98

Thursday."

She laughed at that and he liked the sound of her laughing. Her pretty face lit up with joy, as she forgot about the drudgery of her existence for a few minutes.

'Na, that would be daft but I canna really tell ye exactly what I say, because it micht be dangerous for ye,' he warned direly, knowing the hint of danger would be mildly frightening, but thrilling for her, as well as making him seem more mysterious.

'And... What aboot the Tinker's Kiss? she almost whispered, breathlessly, her eyes wide.

'Ah weel, noo, that's a different thing athegither,' he explained. 'I would claim the Tinker's Kiss, as a reward, or peyment if I'd deen the jobs agreed, and they telt me they had nae money, but only if the lass, say a fermer's wife, or milkmaid, hoosemaid, or hoosekeeper, was affa bonny. I widnae kiss just onny woman. I micht be jist a tinker, but I hae a tinker's pride, and I'm affa particular aboot wha I choose tae kiss.'

'It disnae seem much o' a reward for a' yer hard work, jist to get a wee kiss at the end o' it,' she concluded.

'Ah, maybe to you lass, but it's nae jist onny wee kiss,' he explained, 'it's a Tinker's Kiss, it's very special.' Her eyes opened even wider as he teased her.

'Fit wye is it special?' she asked, her hand going to her face, actually touching her pretty mouth.

Now he knew the signs and knew that if he was clever enough he'd be kissing those lips very soon, and after that, who knows what might happen?

'Weel noo, a Tinkers Kiss; ye'd be as weel trying to explain the wind, or the sun, or the rain,' he said dramatically, his voice dropping lower, pulling her in, making her lean closer to catch his words. 'It's something wild and free, a secret handed doon through a' the generations o' my tinker clan for hundreds o' years, nae to be bestowed on jist onnybody ye ken. I would only gie the Tinker's Kiss tae the bonniest o' women, it's nae suitable for every lass ye understand?'

She nodded her head, still touching her lips with her fingers, her eyes held by his darker ones, which seemed to fill and overcome her senses.

'Aye, I understand noo, I think,' she said breathlessly.

He judged the time was right for her and slowly, as if approaching a wild animal that might flee at any moment, he got up and came round the table to her. She watched, trembling, and turned in her chair to meet him. Looming over her, but never breaking eye contact, he pulled her gently to her feet and enfolded her in his arms. She came willingly, knowing it was wrong but too weak to resist. He smelled of wood-smoke and the wild woods but she felt safe in his arms. He lifted her chin with his hand, his eyes gazing into hers, and whispered to her.

'I give thee the Tinker's Kiss, and bestow upon thee a' good fortune,' and stooping a little, he covered her mouth with his.

His kiss was soft and gentle, parting her lips slowly, kissing her deeply and passionately the way she longed to be kissed, a kiss like no other she had ever had before. She knew she could deny him nothing if he chose to take it. His hands on her body brought her further excitement, caressing gently at first, then more firmly. It felt wonderful; the tenderness of his kiss and gently stroking hands; so wonderful that she no longer cared about anything but this moment.

Now she thought she understood the joy of the Tinker's Kiss as her body seemed to melt and dissolve in a haze of pleasure. She had a momentary pang of conscience, but his kissing and fondling drove any lingering thought of resistance from her mind. She had never, ever, felt this good with her husband and she knew now that he was a very poor lover in comparison to the tinker who was making her feel things she'd never felt before.

They clung to each other for some time, long after their pleasure was sated. There were tears of joy in her eyes when she looked up at him. He kissed her bonny face and told her she was beautiful and held her in his arms for long moments, kissing her eyes and eyelashes, tasting the salt of her tears. Eventually they broke apart; he buttoning his trousers, while she re-arranged her clothes, which were in some considerable disarray.

After a while she said, 'My man will be hame soon.' Suddenly she broke down and wept, her shoulders heaving as she was wracked by huge sobs, and he took her in his arms to comfort her.

'There now my bonny lass, dinna be sae upset. Is he a brute, does he ill-use ye?' he asked.

'Nah, or at least, I dinna think he means tae be, but I micht as weel be one o' his sheep or kye for a' he cares aboot me. I work and cook and clean, but he never notices, and as for his husbandly duties, weel, he has never gien me pleasure like ye jist did, never, ever. A' I ever feel wi him is pain.'

'Come wi me then lass, pack a few things, and come wi me, tak tae the road, and I'll be yer man. I'm nae merriet and nae woman has onny claim on me. I warn ye noo though, it's a hard life. Nae easy.'

She looked up at him, her eyes shining. She smiled wistfully and shook her head as if resigned to her life of drudgery, looking at the floor, and then slowly, her head lifted, and there was a smile on her face, her shoulders straightened, as she looked at him again.

'Really, dae ye mean it? I dinna even ken yer name. Would ye burden yer free and easy life for the likes o' me?' she asked.

'In a minute lass, in a minute, for I've niver felt like

this aboot onny woman until noo. If yer coming, come noo, for we must be far awa afore yer man gets hame, whaur is he onnywye?'

'He's in Aiberdeen, at the cattle mart and winna be hame 'til late - boozy maist likely,' she concluded, and that thought seemed to sweep away any reservations she might have had. 'Wait a minute or twa,' and she ran upstairs, taking her own few bits and pieces and wrapping them in a bundle.

Going into the kitchen she took a frying pan and a small pot, along with the rest of the bacon, a few eggs, and some utensils for cooking with. She left a note; 'I'm away with the raggle taggle gypsies,' before taking one last look around the place.

She thought her heart would burst with joy. She felt free as she locked the door and placed the key under the flower pot at the front door.

Walking down the road together with her new found lover, there was not one single thought of regret in her mind. She never once looked back. The farmer never saw his wife again, although he heard rumours of her being seen from time to time at this fair, or that market, in the company of the tinkers, and always with a tall dark haired man and a babe in arms. She looked happy, they said, and he cursed all tinkers.

13. THE HAUNTED PIPES

This is one of the shortest stories I've collected, but also one of the most interesting, a wee gem, which I got from another cousin, who I regard as an unimpeachable source. She mentioned it to me quite a while ago, when she first heard I was collecting family stories, but it took me ages to get round to asking her again. My fault entirely, but I have the story now, and it's a great little story about a personal possession, an article, that was haunted, rather than a place or person.

'It was aboot half past seven in the morning,' she began, 'I was getting ready tae go oot tae work, and jist sitting at the fireside, beside a nice big fire, tying my shoelaces, and I was bendin' doon tae tie them. The living room door was jist in front of me tae my right. The door opened, and I said, "aye?" and I looked up and saw the person, a man, tae my mind, as clear as onnything. He had a heidful o' thick white hair, a fair height o' person, with a red kind o' top on, but I couldna see onny legs. He walked richt through the door and ower tae where there was an auld chest of drawers, a dresser kind o' thing, jist an auld fashioned dresser. He stopped beside it. I said, "aye?" again, as if tae say, "fa are you," and I looked doon tae finish tying my laces, and when I looked up he was gone, and that was it, that was what I saw.'

I shouted tae my mother. "Ma, fa's that auld man, fa's the man that's in the hoose?"

'There's naebody here,' my mother replied fae the kitchen.

'I saw the man jist now,' I said, 'I definitely seen the man, he's got gray hair, fa is he?'

Well, really and truly there wisnae much mair tae it than that. I seen the man, the person, I could see his face, I could describe him, I can still see him yet, it wis sae clear and vivid in my mind.'

My father was still in bed, so I went through tae him and I said, 'Da, did you see the man that came in?'

'No, there's naebody here,' he replied, repeating what my mother had said.

Of course, I was in a rush because I was gan tae my work, getting ready to catch the bus.

'Da, there's a man wi a gray heid gan aboot in the hoose, ye'd better get up and check.' I said, 'I saw him, I saw him as clear as daylight,' and my father asked me what I saw, so I telt him.

'He had a red top on, and a snow white heid o' hair. He walked in and I was bendin' doon tying my laces. I looked doon and fin I looked up again, he was gone. I canna see him in the hoose, ye'd better get up in case... well the bairns were still in their beds.'

So he jumped oot o' his bed, saying, 'There's naebody

here,' but I was convinced I'd seen somebody.

'I did see him, I saw somebody in the hoose,' I insisted, but by this time it was getting late and I had tae go tae my work, and that was mair or less the end o' the story.

That wis jist fit I saw, but there was maybe a bit o' an explanation tae come later on.

Noo, as it turned oot, my father had been working wi one o' his brithers, and met up wi my uncle later that same day and he happened tae mention that he'd been woken up early that mornin' because I had seen a strange man in the hoose, and described what I'd seen.

'Oh I ken what that wis,' said my uncle, 'that wis the ghost o' the auld man looking for his pipes!'

My uncle was referring to the set of bagpipes my father had bought from him a short while before.

'You've got the man's pipes separated,' my uncle went on, and my da agreed wi whit my uncle said.

'Aye,' he replied, 'yer richt enough, I've got the chanter oot, and it's in a drawer in the dresser.'

'If you separate the pipes, or tak onny bitties aff o' them, ye'll see that man. Folk see him if the pipes are separated, but if the pipes are thegither, the wye they should be, ye dinna see him. I bought the pipes fae a relation o' the man,' he explained, 'he'd been killed in the war, or so they said, and his legs blawn aff. He was teen fae the battlefield, I heard, but died o' his wounds later.'

'That's richt queer,' my da said, 'because my lassie said she hidnae seen his legs, he had nae legs.'

'Well, that's true enough,' she confirmed, 'because I only saw the top half o' him, it was weird, so consciously I'd seen the top half o' a man; but I suppose fin yer a young lassie, bendin' doon tying yer shoelaces, in a hurry, gan awa tae yer work, ye see what ye expect tae see. Although, tae be honest, I *had* said that aboot his legs before I kent the story we got fae my uncle later. I had said tae my ma, that I'd only seen the top half o' him, that he must have been wearing black troosers or something, and it wis weird.

Onnywye I went awa tae my work, but when my father came back that nicht, he collected up the bagpipes including the chanter, put them in their box. He took them back to my uncle the next day and telt him tae sell them for onnything he could get.

'I dinna wint tae keep them in the hoose, the man was here as well, so that's fit wye I selt them on,' said my uncle.

So the upshot wis that the pipes were selt and fa ever has got them noo is welcome tae them,' she said, 'but I winder if wha ever has got them, still sees the man, does this person still come tae them if they separate the pipes? It would be interesting tae ken, but I doot we never will.'

107

14. TWA FERM LOONS

My late father told me this story, set in the 1930's, which took place while he was working on a farm near Inverurie in Aberdeenshire. I can't be more precise about the time, but I suspect it was in the late thirties in the years immediately prior to World War Two. I have added dialogue to give a flavour of the area and times, but the story is substantially the same.

* * *

'Ae Seterday efterneen, me and my best pal Geordie got wirsel's cleaned up; hid a gweed wash, and a scrape o' the dial, clartit wir heids wi hair ile, and heidit intae Inverurie. We didna hae muckle tae spend, maybe a poun' apiece, bit it wis eneugh tae get us awa fae the ferm for the nicht, wi a bittie left ower tae buy wirsel's a couple o' beers an' a pyokie o' chips, syne get the bus back tae the ferm again.

Fin we got intae Inverurie, we heidit for the Butcher's Airms, jist aff the toon square on West North Street. I pushed in aboot the bar, an' efter a filey I managed tae catch the barman's ee an' ordered twa beers. The place wis fair steerin, an' the barmen were sair chauved tae keep up. Lads were shouting orders at them fae a the airts. Maybe 'at's fit wye he gave me change o' a fiver fin I only gied him a poun'. I said nithing, an' put the change in my pooch. Things were lookin up; fae being skint, damn near stoney broke, we noo hid a bit o' siller tae spen. Weel, I lookit ower at Geordie, an' he winkit back tae me, a muckle, daft grin on his face.

'Drink up min, we'll maybe catch the bus an mak for Aiberdeen,' says he.

Noo that we hid some siller, we could afford tae gyang intae the toon, tae Aiberdeen, far there wis an affa lot mair for twa loons like us tae enjoy. So we suppit up oor beer, an' jist as we were heidin for the door, the barman gied me a roar. Weel, my hert fair sank, I thocht the game wis up; he must've noticed that he'd gien me the wrang change, an' winted it back I thocht, but nah, I wis wrang.

'Hey min,' he said 'dinna forget yer coat,' wavin' his airm an pintin tae a coat across the back o' a chair far we'd been sittin.

It wisnae my coat, an' it wisnae Geordie's, bit I thankit him jist the same. I lifted the coat, draipit it ower my airm, an' cerriet it ootside.

'Rin,' said Geordie fin we got ootside, an' I didnae need tae be telt again.

We baith boltit doon the road intae the toon square, for if the coat's owner hid come back we micht hae got done for stealin. Being a Seterday efterneen, the square wis fair hivin we fowk, shoppin and sic like, bit it wisnae lang afore ane o' Jimmy Easton's buses came intae the square, stoppit ootside the toon hall, an' we got on.

It wis a rare day, an it wis a pleasant eneugh rin intae Aiberdeen, especially wi siller in oor pooches. There wis nae hurry noo, for the bars wid a be closed 'til five onywye, an the bus fair took it's time; stoppin here, stoppin there, Kintore, Blackburn, syne Tyrebagger, Bucksburn an ither place in atween. Wifies wi bags an' snottery nosed bairns got aff an' on, parcels for the luggage hole an' God knows fit a. It wis a richt scutter.

Fin we got intae Aiberdeen, the efterneen wis fair k'nipin on, an' me an Geordie hid a dander aboot the streets, finally finding a shop that wid serve oor needs. Fin I left the shop I hid anither thirty bob in my pooch, bit nae coat. The coat wis nae eese tae me, I couldna wear it back in Inverurie, for even though the barman had gien me the coat, it was stolen fin a' wis said and deen. Onywye, the airms wir too short, but it wis a rare Crombie coat, it lookit like new, so the mannie in the pawnshop gave me thirty bob for it. We wis fair loadit wi siller noo an' a ready tae hae a grand nicht fin the pubs opened.

We hid a walkie up Union Street – michty me, fit a crood o' fowk there wis. A kinds, fae posh lookin wifies wi fox furs, an' funcy hats, tae peer lookin aul craturs, shuffling alang, wi shoppin bags an' nae doot sair feet forbye. Weel drest mannie's wearin swankie suits, an' sojers in uniforms, iverybody pushing an' jostling; the fumes aff the traffic nippin wir een an' throats. Horns tootin, engines roarin, horses clip-cloppin, 't'wis enough tae mak ye deef. Me an' Geordie agreed, Aiberdeen was a' richt tae visit, bit surely naebody wid wint tae bide in it.

Oor walk up Union Street brocht us tae the Castlegate, an' being country loons, the ae bit o' Aiberdeen we kent weel wis the Castlegate, for the feein mairket wis held here twice a year. There wis a wifey sellin fruit aff o' a barra, so bein peckish like, I bocht a couple o' peers an a couple of epples. We ate them as we walkit roon the shops in the square, jist lookin intae the windaes, passin the time, but syne we come across a busker mannie playin the fiddle.

He wisnae a great fiddler, ach he scraipit awa weel eneugh, but it was a' the antics he got up tae that kept us amused. He played it ahin his back, atween his legs, roon the back o his heid, twistin this wye an that, gaen fair reed in the face wi some o the shapes he wis getting intae. It didnae dee muckle for the tune, but it wis a rare thing tae see, and gied us a richt lauch.

Drappin a few coppers in his hat we thankit him for the tune an' made tae leave, but he shouted oot tae the crowd tae bide a filey; that he was an escapologist, like the great Harry Houdini, an' if we would only hae patience we wid see a great show. Ha'in nithing better tae dee, we waited a minute or twa, tae see whit wid happen. Weel, he pulled oot a queer looking canvas bag, bit it turned oot it wisnae a bag, it wis a straight jacket, 'Of the type used to restrain dangerous madmen and lunatics,' as he put it.

He teen aff his sark an' simmit, slippit his airms intae the sleeves o' the straight jaiket and askit folk in the crowd that were watchin tae fasten the brass buckles an' thick leather straps doon the back, syne tae fasten the straps attached tae the sleeves roon the back as weel. Next a chiel came ower an' wrappit a chain roon about him, an' padlocked it, again getting fowk fae the crowd tae check the pad lock. They noddit and agreed amongst themsels that the lock wisnae a fake an' that he wis weel lockit in.

He did nithing much for a meenit or twa; just stood there trying the strength an tightness o the jaiket. Suddenly he begun to tae throw himself aboot, twistin and struggling, jinkin this wye an' that, roon an' roon, like a whirlin dervish. Somewye or ither, he managed tae get the chain loused, I dinna ken how, bit it fell tae the grun, an' he followed it doon, rolling about, spinnin aroon, the sweat fair blin'in' him, for it wis a warm day. Getting back tae his feet, he struggled this wye an' that, squirmin an' twistin, up an doon, roon and roon. Syne it wis obvious that he'd gotten one airm free, an' wi that he managed tae push the straight jaiket up an' ower his heid an' wis free at last.

The fowk a whistled and cheered, an' he got a gweed puckle o' change in his tin. We drappit twa shillings in the tin and drifted awa, crossing the square tae the bar, for opening time wis drawin near, gaun by the clock on the toon

112

hoose. We wint tae a pub on the corner o' Marischall Street, The Royal Oak, I think it wis. Weel it wis the Royal Oak efter the war, bit I canna mind if it wis cried the Royal Oak hyne back afore the war.

We didnae hae lang tae wait afore opening time, an alang wi a few ither drouthy lookin worthies, we wint intae the bar. We got oorsels a quiet table in the corner an' ordered twa pints o' beer. This wis the life we thocht, fit mair could a body ask for? A pint of beer, a clay pipe fair stappit wi Bogey Roll, an' a pal tae "news" an pass the time wi. Spik aboot content, we wis like twa pigs in sharn! Efter a while we got anither twa pints an' felt even better.

Syne we struck up a conversation wi ithers in the bar, an' ae chiel wis telling jokes, ane efter the ither. Fit a rare lauch we hid, we thocht he should hiv been on the stage at the Tivoli, so we bocht him a drink as weel, an' by this time, an oor or twa hid passed, an' we hid jist got tae oor third pint o' beer, fin calamity struck. Maybe it wis fate peyin us back fur poochin the wrang change at the Butcher's Airms, an' pawnin the Crombie coat, bit fitiver it wis, it a wint doonhill like a rummle o' bricks.

Some members o' the fairer sex had arrived at the bar, bit we didnae pey them onny heed. Tae say they were nae bonny, would be an ill deserved compliment. Weel, there we wis, minding oor ain business, fin een o' them comes ower by as bold as brass.

'Wid you loons care tae hae some ladies company?' she spiered, sounin as if her nose wis fair stappit. I lookit at her an' her pals, an' so did Geordie. I wis jist aboot tae politely decline her offer, bit Geordie, an' his big mou, wi the help o three pints, got in afore me.

'Nah, quine, niver,' he said. 'We're maybe jist twa country loons, bit we're nae sae daft as tae spend gweed siller on twa hoors, fin we could spend it on drink.'

Weel, she wisnae best pleased.

'Hey yokel,' she replied, 'fa are ye crying a hoor?'

Mysel, I thocht it wis mair fit they cry ane o' them rhetorical questions like, bit Geordie jist wint at it ful tilt.

'You ye bliddy coo-bag – noo leave us tae enjoy wir pint,' adding, 'bugger aff,' for gweed measure, tae add insult tae injury.

Weel, 'at's fin it really wint badly wrang. Some mair insults were exchanged, an' things got a bit heated like, nae tae mention louder, syne ithers in the bar startit tae jine in, an' the quine hit Geordie wi her handbag. Geordie jumpit tae his feet and for his pairt, he wis jist trying tae hud her aff like, but een o' the toonsers thocht Geordie wis gaen tae hit her an' steppit in, throwin a punch, hittin Geordie on the lug.

Geordie pushed her awa, an' she landed on her doup at the ither side o' the bar, syne Geordie gied the lad that punched him a skelp that must've made his heid dirl, for he sat doon, quiet as a moose, his face fair white as chalk.

Anither lad steppit in an' squared up tae Geordie, bit I thocht at wis sleekit kind, so a gweed skelp fae me teen care o' him. Afore we kent far we wis, we were backit intae oor corner takin on a comers, duckin the thrown pint mugs an' chairs.

The barman must hae cried the bobbies, an' they didnae hae far tae come, for the police heidquarters at Lodge Walk wis jist across the road. Being strangers, the fowk in the bar a blamed us for startin it, an' we were taen awa, an' lockit up, an' that wis the end o' oor nicht on the spree. Tae mak metters worse, we were kept the hale weekend in the jile.

On Monday mornin, we wis let oot, an' taen intae the coort. We thocht it best jist tae plead guilty, tae get it ower an' done wi, an' the judge fined us thirty bob each for disturbance o' the peace. We caught the bus for Inverurie later that morning, an' got hame by dennertime. The fermer wisnae best pleased an' we hid tae work late that nicht, an' the nicht efter tae mak up for't. Oot o' the money we hid, nane wis left. Oor pooches were as bare as bare could be, an' that, as they say, concludes my story o' twa ferm loons on the spree.

I have to be honest and say, I don't get on buses very often. They're too slow and inconvenient, and depending on whether the driver is early or late, they either dawdle along or stop altogether while the driver reads his newspaper, or are driven too fast when the driver has to make up time, often braking ferociously when they reluctantly stop to pick up passengers. Even at their best they aren't as convenient as a car, but just occasionally I will get on one, usually when my car is in the garage being repaired, or serviced, and I need to get back home from the garage, or go back to the garage to pick it up again. That's what happened on that fateful day when *she* came back into my life again.

'She,' was the love of my life. I've loved very few women over the years, but I have never loved anyone like I loved her. I think she ruined me for other women; I compared them all to her, and one by one they came up lacking, but I eventually had to come to terms with that and live my life as best I could without her.

We spent a wonderful nine months together and she made me so incredibly happy, happier than I'd ever been and happier than I've ever been since. I thought of nothing else but her all day long. I was in love. We spoke together for hours that seemed like minutes, laughed together, and I gloried in her company. She simply made me more than I was. I thought any day when I didn't see her was a day wasted and I felt like part of me was missing. But then things started to go wrong.

Bit by bit, little by little, she began to 'distance' me, fobbing me off with excuses. When I suggested we meet, she was too busy, or she couldn't manage. I was so incredibly hurt and confused. From being a loving, fun companion, who told me she loved me, she rarely smiled for me any more and it was her smile that had lifted my heart always. Her smile was a thing of rare beauty that lit up her face and made my heart beat a whole lot faster. I lived for her smile but now, for some inexplicable reason, it had faded. Her beautiful brown eyes no longer shone for me but instead looked right through me, with no hint of the woman I loved behind them.

This inevitably led to tensions between us and I was so unbelievably hurt that I actually felt physical pain. I did the stupid 'manly' thing and lashed out blindly; not physically I hasten to add, just verbally; telling her I was sick of being pushed away when I had done nothing to deserve it. Suddenly, with that, it was all over. She wouldn't listen to me or speak to me any more. I tried to get her to talk to me, to discuss it. I knew if we could only sit down together to speak about it, I could make everything right again, but she point blank refused and no amount of pleading or begging seemed to get through to her. That was it, it was all over.

I tried and tried to make things right, I apologised and said I was sorry, even when I didn't have a clue what I was saying sorry for, but the more I tried the worse it became until eventually, if we met somewhere, she would totally ignore me and pretend I wasn't even there. For my part, I was still in love, still besotted. I was convinced my life was over, things would never be right again.

Night after night I lay sleepless in my bed, crying silently, tears streaming from my eyes, thinking of her, speaking to her again as if she was there, whispering to her, just to hear the sound of her name. I grieved for my loss, I longed to see her, speak to her. She filled my thoughts as much as ever but now it was all tied up in loss, a sense of ruin, and utter, excruciating pain. I couldn't see a way out of it, any way forward, and I'm not ashamed to say, I momentarily thought of ending it all. But I had family to consider, family I loved, and the thought of being so selfish as to hurt them held me back.

If there was some magic button, I thought, a button that I could press, to end it all as if I had never existed, a bit like Jimmy stewart in that old Christmas film, 'It's A Wonderful Life,' and not leave some hellish mess behind, then I would have pressed it gladly to end the hurt and pain.

I never got over her and I know now, I never will. She still haunts my thoughts when I see a place we used to go, or smell a familiar perfume, or hear a particular song, and the hurt crowds back into my heart, momentarily overwhelming me with regret. I know in my heart, I'll love her until I die and although I've had to carry on, there will always be a special place in my heart for her. Nobody could ever replace her and I know now, even with the passage of the years, that nobody ever will.

I can only hope that my explanation will go some way towards setting the scene for you, a small insight perhaps. An understanding of what took place in the years before and why I acted as I did on the day I saw her again.

As I said previously, I rarely take the bus, which is why it seemed such an amazing coincidence on that particular day that she should get on that particular bus at the same time as me.

I was sitting there, mildly bored, daydreaming, when the bus stopped with a jerk, waking me from my reverie. As I looked up I saw her. My heart raced with excitement, completely involuntary, as she walked up the aisle towards me, engrossed in looking for a vacant seat. She didn't notice me, and sat down two seats in front of me - leaving me staring at the back of her head. My mouth felt as dry as an old boot and I could hardly breathe.

As I sat there wondering what to do next, she looked out of the window affording me a look at the face I had once loved so completely. She was still beautiful, although I could see some strands of silver in her dark hair and there was a few fine lines around her eyes, what they call 'laughter lines.' I thought with huge relief that the intervening years had been very kind to her; there was no loss in her loveliness, not in my eyes anyway. Although she had been cruel to me, I could never believe, stupidly perhaps, that she had meant to be deliberately cruel and I would have hated it if she had aged badly with the years. I had carried a mental picture of her in my head for all this time, and I was glad to see her beauty undiminished.

Should I speak to her? I was confused, undecided, and almost spoke her name out loud to draw her attention but held myself back. What good could come of it, I asked myself, apart from maybe seeing her wonderful smile again? Her mere presence was overwhelming me emotionally, as all the old feelings came flooding back. Memories, loss, hurt, mixed emotions, crowded in, one upon the other.

If I spoke, what would she say? Would she be pleased to see me after all this time I wondered? Would it be stiff and awkward, neither of us knowing what to say? So, I took the cowards way out, and said nothing. Instead I studied what I could see of her face. Once again, I was completely absorbed by her features the way I used to be. I looked at her perfectly shaped lips and mouth, and mused to myself.

This was the mouth that I was ever eager to kiss, the mouth that spoke to me quietly and intimately of everything under the sun for hours on end. The mere sound of her voice made me feel good, dare I say it, just the sound of her voice excited me. This mouth that above all else spoke of love to me, that had told me she loved me, that laughed and smiled as we spoke, that stole, then destroyed my heart.

I let my memory wander back through the years, remembering all the great times we had shared together. That special and wonderful day we had spent, in that little country town, which I often think of with the greatest of pleasure and nostalgia, although now, even that pleasure is bitter sweet and tainted by the hurt that followed so very soon after. I cast my memory back, and I think of the intimate dinner we shared that same evening, and how, looking across the table, her eyes and her smile was all I could see, and with those sparkling brown eyes holding mine, the rest of the people in the restaurant didn't seem to exist. There was a, 'bubble,' which encapsulated us as we looked into each other's eyes, her smiles, the laughter, the closeness, and the love.

I treasure that day in my memory, as the high water mark of our relationship, for it was never to be repeated. I had thought at the time there would be many more days like this in the years ahead, and our love could only deepen and grow. Poor deluded, love-struck fool that I was, for just a few short weeks later she grew colder and harder, becoming distant and hurtful, almost destroying me as a consequence. Despite all of that, I knew there would always be a special place for her in my heart, and in my affections.

I speculated what she might think if the roles were reversed and it was *her* sitting behind me, with me unawares, sitting two seats in front of her. Would her heart beat faster as mine was at this precise moment, at the mere sight of *her*? Would she care even just the slightest bit, would *she* speak up, and make me aware that she was behind me? Would *she* be thinking of the great times we shared? Were they still important memories in her mind, did she even remember them at all, I wondered? Or perhaps like me, she'd realistically think that too much time had passed and nothing could be gained by re-opening so many old wounds and memories.

All these thoughts raced through my mind as I looked at her reflection in the window. My stomach was churning, there was a tightness in my chest that I remembered oh so well. It was hurt, and acute longing... and love; longing for a love that might have been, a love that should have matured into something much more, longing for a love and a life that was irretrievably lost, and had never been and yet should have been. A wonderful life we should be spending together, loving and caring for each other and yet for some inexplicable reason that I had never understood, it had all been taken from me.

I realised in that instant that I had never come to terms with her loss, I had *never* stopped loving her, and I never would; I would go to my grave loving her still. I felt my eyes fill up once again at the thought of that loss but I rebuked myself, desperately trying to regain control, telling myself not to be so silly. It was gone and yet I couldn't help but feel completely, and utterly desolate.

As the bus slowly began to move away from the previous bus-stop, I realised she was getting ready to get up from her seat. This was my last chance I thought, but instead of calling her name, or even getting up and getting off the bus too, I just sat there, dumbly, watching her stand up and move slowly down the aisle to the front of the bus.

The doors slid back with a rattle and she alighted gracefully. She moved away, but just a step or two, as she took stock of her belongings, handbag and shopping bag, adjusting her scarf and coat.

I couldn't take my eyes off her. I was hungry for more, a last sight of her before she disappeared from my life once again. New passengers filed onto the bus, shuffling up the aisle, but I had eyes only for her. She looked up, just a casual glance, and our eyes met and locked. I saw the recognition in her eyes and the wonderful, warm, smile that always lifted my heart with joy was mine again. Her face lit up and I knew I was smiling from ear to ear like some demented fool. Then the bus gave a shudder and very, very slowly began to move away from the bus-stop.

She stepped forward, still smiling, and reaching out,

touched the glass of the window, as if she was reaching to touch my face affectionately as she had in days gone by. I reached out too, and touched the inside of the glass where her fingers were. She took one, then two steps, moving with the bus, her beautiful brown eyes holding mine, a wistful, sad look on her face as her smile faded. Then the bus picked up speed and she was gone. I looked back and saw her give a little hesitant wave as she grew smaller in the distance, and I watched her until she was out of sight.

I sat there, heart sick, with that familiar feeling of hopeless loss wrenching at my gut once again, until it was time for me to get off the bus too. As she had so many times before, she filled my thoughts to the exclusion of everything else. I sat down, or slumped rather, on a pavement bench, and just sat there, my head in my hands, thinking about her, completely bereft, an emotional wreck, tears in my eyes. Why didn't I speak you may ask, because believe me I've asked myself that same question a thousand times.

It was all about hurt – she had hurt me so very badly, and as much as I had loved her, and despite the years in between, I knew it would only take a matter of a few minutes talking to her, seeing her smile, laughing with her, before all that love, sheer need and want of her came flooding back again. I would have been happy to try, for loving her again would be all too easy for me, but I could never trust her not to do the same again. I'd be straight back into that world of hurt and pain that she had inflicted on me once before. I knew I wouldn't be able to survive it this time. I was too old, too fragile, and too needy perhaps, and too aware of my own shortcomings to think any sort of reunion would ever succeed.

Never? Well, as the old saying goes, 'Never say never,' for who knows what the future brings? If having seen me again, she made some attempt to contact me, I know I would agree to meet her. Yes, even knowing the danger I would be in, for her hold on me is still so strong, and even after all these years that have passed, there's a special place within my heart I'll keep for her until the day I die.

16. THE GRAY LADY O' LUMPHANAN

This is a story I got from one of my cousins who stays in the town of Montrose, in Angus, Scotland. Montrose is the home town of choice for many of Scotland's travelling families, and I have many cousins and relatives there. When I appealed to my relatives for family stories, this was a story that came as a result of that appeal. My cousin told me this ghostly tale in a quiet, matter of fact way, and although she was just seven years old at the time the story took place, I have no reason whatsoever to doubt it, or her.

'We had been doon in Blairgowrie at the berries,' she began, 'and when we finished there, we had travelled intae Fife.'
After the family had been in Fife for a wee while, working and hawking, they had returned to Aberdeenshire, and set up camp at Lumphanan, on Deeside.

The family had been out visiting relatives, her father's elder brother and his wife, who lived just a few miles away on the outskirts of Banchory. After spending a pleasant few hours, catching up on all the 'news,' about the rest of the family they had come home late in the evening to their campsite at Lumphanan. Her father fancied a cup of tea before bedtime but her mother told him he couldn't get a cup of tea because they'd run out of milk. There were still lights on up at the farm, she pointed out, so, if he wanted tea, he'd have to go up to the farm they were camped near and see if the farmer would sell them some milk for their tea, otherwise they'd get no tea at breakfast time either.

'I canna dee that,' he replied, ever mindful of how travellers were perceived by the settled country folk, and how careful a man had tae be when going near a farm late at night.

'If the fermer's nae at hame, it would be shan (bad) for me to ging tae the door. His wife or his lassies wid maybe be feart o' a strange man coming tae the door late at nicht. I want a cup o' tea bit I'll jist hae tae, "want," I doot.'

However, his wife immediately had a solution for that.

'Look, jist ging up tae the ferm, and tak some o' the lassies wi ye, and they can ging tae the door. Surely tae god, if ye stand weel back, they'd hae nithing tae be feart aboot wi a man that's got twa or three lassies wi him,' and so, given that sensible advice, that was what they did.

'Now, why on earth my father didna tak the car up tae the ferm I dinna ken, but it was a fine, clear nicht in the late summer and he decided we would walk up tae the ferm and so we set oot walkin'. We had a wee enamel milk pail, with a close fitting lid, that we used tae hae back in those days, which held about a pint or two, for carrying the milk.'

Full darkness comes on slowly in these northern latitudes in the late summer or early autumn and although it

127

was getting late, it wasn't quite dark yet, but the light was definitely failing. As they walked up the road they became aware of a woman some distance ahead. She was walking at the opposite side of the road from them but slowly coming towards them. As the distance between them decreased, in the near darkness her father thought the woman looked like one of his sisters who lived nearby.

'That woman looks affa like my sister,' he said to the two lassies who were walking beside him. 'I doot she and her auld man have been arguing and she's oot walkin tae cool doon.'

So, thinking it was his sister, he called out to her.

'Whit are ye dee'in oot here this late at nicht?' he called out, but at the same time thinking it a bit strange that his sister was here at all.

He waited a few seconds for her reply, but none came. The woman said nothing, so he called out to her again and this time he identified himself to her in case she didn't know who it was in the bad light. All the time the distance was decreasing and they were drawing closer. The woman still said nothing and didn't even look towards them.

'Well, I was only seven,' she said, 'so thinking it really was my auntie, I ran ower to speak tae her, but of course it wasn't my auntie. My father called out to me: 'Come here lassie, come here, that's nae my sister, it's something nae richt, it's a ghost,' he warned, but by this time I was standing

128

richt in front o' the ghost, and believe me, it was a ghost. I can always remember looking doon at her feet and she was wearing funny auld fashioned shoes, wi lang pinted taes, and her dress was richt doon tae her ankles. She was wearing a shawl as well. I looked up tae the face and she was lookin' doon at me, I got a richt fear. It was an aulder, grey, haired woman, it was definitely a woman. Her eyes were red, and I looked up at her for a few seconds, she was staring doon at me, but I quickly looked awa again, because I heard my father shouting tae me, 'Come awa fae that woman, it's something nae richt lassie.'

'He was coming ower the road tae get me but I ran back tae him as fast as my wee leggies could move, and I got in really close beside my father and sister. 'I telt ye nae tae go near that thing, didn't I tell you? When I shout tae ye tae come back, you'd better come back,' he said. I was only seven years auld, jist a bairn, but he was mair worried aboot me than angry.

'Dinna look at her, dinna look at her, jist keep walkin',' my father warned us, drawin' me and my sister close in aboot him, but did I nae turn and look back at her?

'Well, it had started tae follow us, but now it was floating, it came right past us, and it floated away up high intae the sky while we stood and looked at it. It floated awa like a balloon would.

'The next day we went up to see dad's sister, and he

asked her if she'd been oot the night before, walking on that bit o' road, but she replied that she would never be out walking on the road in the dark. We never found oot onny thing else aboot it, it was just a mystery, a ghost, so that's the end o' my story.'

17. TWA HERTS ENTWINED

I got the idea for this story from the song of the same name, which I wrote in 2007. The inspiration for the song was a walk I took round Seaton Park in Aberdeen one morning, and like the first lines of so many traditional songs, it was a, 'bright May morning.' The park follows the natural contours of the land and you can either walk straight down into the lower part or walk along the top path, which circles the natural amphitheatre that forms the park. I took the top path, which is flanked by mature trees growing on the steep slope of the, 'amphitheatre.' Many of these trees are beech trees, with that wonderful silvery bark and I noticed that over many years, young lovers had carved their names and symbolic hearts to show their love. I thought that young lovers probably don't do that any more; it's all done on the internet, on social media. That was the inspiration for the song, and through that, this story.

* * *

I'll never forget the wonderful and momentous day my love and I became lovers in the truest sense of the word. We had been 'walking out' together for quite some time, had gradually gotten to know each other and eventually fallen in love. I adored her and, for her part, the feeling seemed to be entirely mutual.

She was tall, almost as tall as me, with a slim but

womanly figure, dark hair, thick and glossy. Nineteen years old to my twenty five years and possessing a fine mind too. She was no frivolous, empty head, she had common sense aplenty and the light of intelligence and humour shone from her wonderful dark eyes. She was, to my mind, someone to be treasured, someone to nurture and be nurtured by, my ideal life partner.

There was an unspoken, 'understanding' that we would marry; there never was any doubt in either of our minds about that. It just felt the right thing for both of us but, above all else, it was because we loved each other.

We were, 'walking out,' one fine Saturday afternoon in the late spring. It was a lovely day and we were holding hands, with me occasionally slipping my arm around her slim waist, pulling her closer, and kissing her cheek from time to time, stopping to kiss her wonderful mouth a little more intimately before walking on again. Gradually, stopping to kiss took over from walking, until we looked around for somewhere to sit. We found a lovely secluded grassy spot beneath an ancient beech tree and settled ourselves down. We talked and laughed, feeling as if we were the only two people in the entire world under the canopy of the sheltering trees.

For quite some time now we had gradually become more intimate with each other, our kissing and fondling becoming ever bolder but today, for some reason, our restraint crumbled and things took their much delayed natural course, until we finally consummated our love beneath the shade of that tree. It was a truly wonderful moment for both of us, made all the more perfect by the deep love and affection we had built up over the preceding months. When I asked her afterwards if she had any regrets, she laughed.

'My only regret is that we waited sae lang,' she laughed again, and then. 'Fit aboot you, are ye regretting that you've maybe gotten a, "scarlet woman," noo?'

She was laughing as she said it, but I thought there was a wee element of self-doubt there that needed reassuring.

'Nae even a wee bittie, Katie my darling, you're my true love, you're a' my happiness and joy wrapped up in one bonny parcel. Never doot me my love... never,' I emphasised.

I took her in my arms again to reinforce my love for her, and she melted into my embrace.

Soon, the site of our first lovemaking became a regular meeting place and, one day, filled with my feelings of love for her, I took out my penknife and I carved two entwined hearts into the silver bark of 'our' tree, with our initials. She laughed when she saw it and said I was daft but kissed me and thanked me in the best possible way.

There was one 'fly' in our ointment which was causing us problems and that was money, or the lack of it, to be more

133

precise. I was working as a clerk with one of the shipping companies based in Aberdeen but the wages were very poor, not nearly enough for us to set up house and finally get married as we were desperate to do. I searched around for other jobs with a better salary, but there seemed to be nothing for which I was qualified, or anything which could substantially increase my income, until one day a friend drew my notice to an advert in the local paper for the Hudson Bay Company, in the far North of Canada.

Over the course of the next month or so, my love and I discussed this possibility thoroughly, for neither one of us wanted to be parted from the other. Eventually we came to see that if we wanted to marry and live comfortably, there was no other option except for me to 'seek my fortune' elsewhere. The result was that I applied for a position with the Hudson Bay Company, was interviewed and accepted, and within a month or so I was heading across the sea to Canada.

Our parting had been distressing to say the least. I took my leave of her beneath the tree that we thought of as, our special tree. Sitting on a tartan travel rug, spread out on the grass.

'I ken ye hiv tae leave,' she sobbed, 'and ye're deein it for us, but my hert's fair broken at the thocht. Fit am I gaen tae dee withoot ye? Fit am I gaen tae dee?'

Her sobbing was heart rending for me too and I admit

there were tears in my eyes as I held her tightly, never wanting to let her go, never wanting to be parted from my love.

'I'll come back tae ye my love,' I promised. 'Have nae doot aboot that, jist promise me ye'll wait for me, ye must promise noo.'

She looked up at me then, tears filling her eyes, the long eyelashes wet with her tears.

'I promise. I *will* wait for you, I promise,' she sobbed, and then she sealed her promise with a kiss.

If I had known at that moment how long it would be before I saw my darling again, I would never have left her in Aberdeen. I would rather have lived in relative poverty than have lived so long without her and without seeing her bonny face.

After arriving at Hudson Bay, I settled into a routine of work, sleep and work. I didn't socialise much, preferring to spend my free time reading and studying whatever books could be found around the settlement. After all I reasoned, I was here to save money, not to spend it and, not being a drinker, it was easier for me than some of the other people working there.

With the early onset of the harsh and bitterly cold Canadian winter there was even less to do but given the lifestyle I had chosen, which was to keep myself to myself and work as much as possible, the weather didn't bother me too much except when I was travelling between my workplace and the rooms I had rented in the settlement.

I wrote and sent letters home to my sweetheart of course. I was missing her terribly and my dearest possession was the photograph I had of her beautiful smiling face. There was nothing much to tell her about Hudson Bay except that it was freezing cold, covered in snow, and that we had been told to watch out for polar bears. They are it seems, the only type of bear to treat humans as prey and will kill and eat humans as a matter of course. I was also told by a fur trapper, whether it is true or not, a horror story that they didn't actually kill you and eat you. They just attacked you and ate you, whether you were still alive or not. The utmost horror of that thought kept me ever vigilant as I made my way between where I was lodging and my place of work, because being so far north, it was dark for most of the day.

With the coming of spring I decided that another winter in Hudson Bay was simply unbearable, so I looked for some way to get out, yet I didn't want to spend too much of my hard earned savings. I heard there had been a gold strike in Australia, away on the other side of the world and the idea that I should perhaps try my luck on the Australian gold fields appealed to me. At least it would be warm and the chances of being eaten alive by a bear simply didn't exist. Another old timer, who came into the store regularly and who had seen a fair bit of the world on his travels, advised me to get myself to a major seaport and sign aboard any ship that would take me closer to my goal. So it was that two months later I was aboard a merchant ship 'The Lydia,' bound for Rio De Janeiro. Now I would be earning money, as well as getting closer to my goal, without spending any more of my savings.

Life aboard 'The Lydia' was hard, especially for someone like myself who wasn't a qualified, or experienced seaman. Along with a few others, I was at best a general labourer and spent my time doing all the menial jobs that were at the bottom of the ladder. Sometimes there was an element of danger, like stowing and making safe, cargo that had broken loose in the holds when the seas became rough, but it was a case of keeping your wits about you and doing the job as quickly and as safely as we could. The regular crew were generally decent types but of course there are always bullies in whatever walk of life you choose and the ship was no different. As usual, I kept my head low and got on with the job.

As we steamed south the weather became noticeably warmer until one day we were all called up on deck. The Captain announced that we were about to cross the equator, and it was an old seafaring tradition that King Neptune had to be appeased, so any crew member who had not already crossed must be initiated into this honourable company. There followed a rather predictable, and nonsensical, 'men at

137

sea,' pseudo ceremony in which those like myself were subjected to various indignities. All in good fun they told me, and for the sake of appearances, I went along with it, while thinking the whole thing rather silly. I'm not one given over to superstitions or rustic humour.

Eventually the ship docked in Rio and I stayed on board for a few days, helping to facilitate the unloading and various other tasks, with my experience as a shipping clerk coming in very handy. Most of the crew, when not needed, went ashore to sample the flesh pots of Rio, coming back to the ship whenever they got sober enough to remember where the ship was. For myself, I stayed on board until the last possible moment before it sailed again. I ventured into the city for a few hours, at one point, just to see the sights, and I have to admit, the Brazilian ladies reputation for great beauty was not undeserved but I looked at them and I knew that none could compare with my own darling girl back home in Aberdeen. I was not tempted.

In that week or so in port I had visited a number of shipping agencies and managed to sign on with another merchant ship, this time heading for Australia, and so it was that as the old 'Lydia' made ready to sail, I took my leave of the friends I had made in the crew, thanked the captain and officers for having me aboard and made my way down the gangplank, ready for the next adventure.

Before leaving Rio I had a walk in one of the local

parks. Finding a secluded spot and a suitable tree, I once again carved two hearts entwined and our names into the bark. I had done the same before leaving Canada and it had become part of my routine now. I had determined that no matter where I went, I would carve our names on the bark of a tree, to declare our love for each other. Although I knew it was a matter of indifference to the rest of the world, to me it meant a great deal. Silly I know, but sometimes love can make us behave irrationally and it was harming nobody else.

The passage to Australia was pretty much uneventful, apart from the time we spent steaming round Cape Horn. Its reputation was well deserved, the seas were heavy and very rough, to say the least, as we ploughed through the mountainous waves with almost gale force winds whistling through the rigging. But we were soon past the worst and moving into the calmer waters of the Pacific. After that, the voyage, as I have already mentioned, was straight forward and uneventful, until one bright sunny morning the captain told us that the land we could see on the horizon off the starboard side was Australia and we'd be steaming into Sydney harbour by the end of the day.

Once again I stayed on board as long as I could and again managed to put my experience as a shipping clerk to use, helping with cargo manifests and such like, but soon I had to take my leave once more as they made ready to sail. Although I had been working aboard the ship, I had also had put what leisure time I had to good use, scanning the local newspapers, and striking up conversations with people I met, asking them for any news of the gold strikes or gold fields. Based on what information I could glean from the newspapers and the opinions expressed by those I talked to, I decided on impulse to head for a mining town in South Australia called Teetulpa, which was a few miles north of another more established town called Yunta.

It could have been north of Timbuctoo for all the difference it meant to me. I'd never heard of either before, but, it seems that was the place to be, so I caught a train the next day and headed for Teetulpa. According to all the reports there had been some rich strikes there but of course that also meant that it was one of the most overcrowded gold-fields in Southern Australia.

I had no illusions about prospecting for gold but I knew that wherever there were gold finds there was money to be made. Just the mere fact that there was gold to be discovered meant that many of the businesses in the area found it hard to retain workers. I'd heard that they were paying premium high wages, but because of the 'gold-fever' with everyone hoping to strike it lucky and become rich, they still couldn't get workers to remain in employment with them for any length of time. I was going to have a look around and try to hire myself out to the highest bidder. I could always go prospecting on my days off if need be, I mused.

Teetulpa turned out to be a hot, dusty, sprawling slum of tents and wooden huts and shacks, interspersed with some more permanent looking and substantial buildings lining the streets. All appeared hastily thrown together to accommodate the needs of the would be miners. I made for the general store, knowing that all the miners would have to frequent it to get their supplies, whether light mining equipment, shovels, picks, etc., as well as food and I was right, it was very busy. Two harassed looking clerks were trying to cope with the orders. It was obvious from the steadily rising tempers of the would-be miners that they simply couldn't keep up, however, they had no option but to struggle manfully on.

A woman who I took to be in her early thirties age – wise; handsome, rather than pretty; came out of what I presumed was the back store, wrapping an apron around her waist and immediately launched herself into the fray. It was obvious within minutes that she was the boss by the way she took charge. I made a note of it, because she was the one I needed to see. After a cursory look around the store, I left, deciding to wait until things had quietened down a bit before offering myself for employment. In the meantime, I had a look around the 'town' such as it was, to gather some more information and try to find somewhere to sleep for my first night. I quickly discovered that it was well-nigh impossible to find anything. With so many prospectors flooding into the town on a daily basis, accommodation was scarce and very, very expensive. I determined that if I was to work in the store and not spend all my wages on living expenses, then I would need to find somewhere to sleep.

Back at the store, things were much quieter than they had been earlier, as I hoped they would be. The woman I had presumed was the boss was no longer serving behind the counter but was stacking shelves with fresh merchandise.

'Good afternoon,' I began, 'I was here a little earlier, but you were so busy, I thought I'd come back when it was a little quieter.'

She looked at me, her blue eyes looking me over quickly, calculating, assessing.

'We're always busy, how can I help you. Are you another one looking to get rich quick?' she asked, the faintest beginning of a smile on her face.

I changed my mind, I had thought her 'handsome' rather than pretty on first inspection but she was actually very pretty when she smiled. She had good even teeth, a full lipped mouth, and those striking blue eyes too.

'Nae really,' I replied, quickly trying to amend my Aberdeen accent so I could be understood.

I had to learn to moderate my accent in the months I'd been in Hudson Bay and aboard the ships.

'It would be nice to be rich of course, but scrabbling aboot in the dirt, the dust, and the heat, and being bitten by every type of flying and creeping insect isn't something I find attractive. I am however, an experienced shipping clerk, and I've heard that most businesses, like this one of yours, is desperately short of staff, and willing to pay good wages. If that's true, and from what I saw earlier it would appear to be the case, then perhaps you would consider taking me on?'

Speech finished, I waited for her verdict. She gave me another one of her smiles, but she had a more interested look on her face this time.

'Well, I certainly could use someone like you if what you say is true. Let's go through to my office, and you can tell me a bit more about yourself. Just let me finish this first, and then we'll have a chat,' she concluded, finishing her task within minutes before turning to me. 'Okay, just come through,' and as she said it, she lifted a hinged section of the counter she was standing behind, motioned me through and I followed her behind the counter and through the door I had seen her appear from earlier in the day.

Her office was small and functional although I could see straight away that her filing system wasn't up to scratch. Papers were piled high, on the desk and on the floor, everywhere in fact.

'Sorry, things are a bit of a mess but there's only so much hours in the day and I'm trying to run this business, with everything that entails, ordering stock, stock control, absolutely everything myself, as well as doing the work of a sales assistant. The paper work has gotten out of hand. Maybe you can help with that if you're any good? Tell me what you've done before,' she asked, getting right down to business.

So, I gave her a brief resume of my career to date; my experience as a shipping clerk in Aberdeen, my time with the Hudson Bay company, the little bit of relevant experience I had in helping both ships I had sailed in with their cargo manifests and so forth. She nodded as I ran through what I had done, smiling all the while. She would never have made a good poker player, I could see that she was happy with what she was hearing.

'Alright, that sounds fine to me, when can you start?' she asked, making a snap decision.

'Well, there's nothing stopping me from starting right now, except I have nowhere to stay, and perhaps we should talk about my wages?' I suggested smiling at her.

'Well, I could dither, and argue about a shilling here and there, but I like to think I'm a fair person,' and she named a figure which was more than twice what I earned as a shipping clerk back home in Aberdeen.

'There's a big storeroom through the back. If you'd be happy to sleep there, then we could try that for a week or so, just to see how it goes. However, if you turn out to be a boozer, or unreliable, then you'll have to get out and find somewhere else to live. I can't have irresponsible people, "living in," with hundreds of pounds of stock all around them. You understand my position on that?' she demanded, sounding quite stern for the first time, no longer smiling.

I agreed at once, assuring her that I wasn't much of a drinker and I didn't smoke, so there was no chance of me starting a fire from a carelessly discarded cigarette or some such. The smile was back on her face again.

'Well, that all sounds fine. Consider yourself hired, let's shake on it,' and she reached out a slim elegant hand for me to shake.

She had a good firm grip, and with that, I was hired.

'I am Mrs Davidson. There's no Mr Davidson, he passed away of a fever three years ago. You may call me Sarah if you wish, when we are working together in the office, and when you know me a bit better, but in the shop I am always to be referred to as Mrs Davidson.'

I nodded in agreement and said how sorry I was for her loss. I also added that I quite understood that propriety had to be maintained at all times in front of the customers and the other staff. She smiled again.

She took me through to the shop and introduced me to the sales assistants, a tall dark haired Englishman called Charlie, who looked reasonably intelligent, if a bit aloof and a red-haired Irishman by the name of Patrick.

'Just call me Paddy,' he urged, 'everybody else does.'

He was a smiler. The lady customers would love him, I

thought.

She informed them that my first duty was to the clerical side of things, working in the office but when they were busy as they had been earlier and 'all hands were needed on deck' then I would double up as a sales assistant behind the counter and help them out. They seemed pleased with the thought that their lives may be made a bit easier by my presence.

Back in the office, she spread her arms indicating the paperwork with a smile.

'It's all yours, I'm delighted to inform you. Make some order out of the chaos, so I can make better decisions about what needs ordered and what not; but first come through to the storeroom and I'll show you where you'll be living,' she said, indicating that I should follow her.

I followed her back through the door that led to the store. Instead of turning left into the shop, she turned right and led me through another door into the back of the shop, to the store room. Between the shop and the storeroom a set of stairs led upwards.

She saw me looking up the stairs but there was no clue as to where the stairs led, there being merely a, 'landing,' to be seen where the stairs doubled back on themselves, leading upwards to another floor.

'Those stairs needn't concern you,' she explained. 'Those are my private rooms, where I live. You only go up there if you're invited for some reason, or need me urgently on some business matter and I'm not in the shop. If that's the case, you knock on the door, and wait for me to reply. I like my privacy,' she added.

I nodded, my understanding, following her into the back store.

The back store, as she called it, was an enormous barn of a room with boxes of various items piled high and goods of every kind on the shelves. She took me to a far corner of the room and suggested that this might be a good place to set myself down.

'If we clear away some of these boxes, we could make enough space for you to sleep here and you'd be able to maybe get an old chest of drawers for your clothes and a few bits and pieces to make it more comfortable for yourself. The outhouse is through that door, but please be aware that you need to keep it locked at *all* times.' She emphasised the, 'all.'

Then added by way of explanation, 'we've had a few less than savoury characters, well criminals actually, desperate to get free supplies trying to break in and help themselves before now, so you must lock the door, even if you're only going to the outhouse for a minute or two.'

I assured her that I would be very careful and she gave me a key which she produced from her apron pocket.

'Don't lose it. If you do, I'll have to change the locks, and guess who's going to pay for that. I'll give you one clue, it

147

won't be me.'

She smiled, I soon found out it was always her way to say the, 'bad,' things with a little smile to sweeten the more bitter medicine.

'Well, I'll leave you to get on with making yourself comfortable. I'll find some sheets and blankets for you, not that you'll need blankets most of the time out here but sometimes it can get cold in the night.'

She turned and, always busy, left me to make the best of it.

I spent the last remains of the day sweeping out the dusty corner of the storeroom which was to become my home for the foreseeable future, trying to make it habitable for myself. First I gathered a number of empty wooden packing cases and formed them into a platform which would become the base of my 'bed' and then I found a number of sacks which I stuffed with the old straw that had been used as protective packing materials for the more fragile incoming goods. There wasn't nearly enough, so I went down the street to a local stable and asked the owner if he'd sell me some more straw to do the job. He asked an exorbitant price, but after a bit of haggling, I managed to get a more reasonable price, and taking it home, entered the storeroom by the back door again.

While I had been out, Sarah, my new boss had obviously visited and left the promised sheets and blankets, and even included a pillow. An old table had appeared with a jug full of water and a basin for washing in. I finished stuffing the sacks with straw and laying them on top of the packing cases, I now had somewhere to lay my head for the night. I thought it was looking quite comfortable and at least it was dry and out of the wind and any possible rain. It had the added bonus of there being no possible chance of being torn limb from limb and eaten by a polar bear.

Next morning I was up bright and early, ready to commence my new duties. When I came through into the office, Sarah asked me if I'd had anything for breakfast. I shook my head, explaining that I hadn't had the time to get anything supplies wise.

'I thought that might be the case. I'll be back in a minute,' and true to her word, she returned from her own apartment with a large bowl of hot porridge and a cup of tea.

When I expressed my surprise and gratitude, she explained. 'I made extra this morning, I thought you might not have had anything. I won't get the best out of you with your stomach empty and rumbling all day.'

I thanked her profusely, for I was indeed very hungry, having had very little to eat the day before due to my travels and making arrangement for employment and all that I've already mentioned.

When I was finished she took the dishes away and I thanked her for her kindness, telling her the porridge was delicious which it was. Most non-Scots don't know how to make porridge, they make it far too thick and lumpy but hers was perfect. When I said that to her, she just smiled sadly and told me her late husband, Mr Davidson, was a Scot, he'd loved his porridge in the morning, so she'd had years of practice making it just the way he liked it.

I gave her my condolences again but she glossed over it, just saying he'd been gone three years past, obviously not wanting to dwell on her loss. I felt sorry for her of course, she seemed such a nice kind woman, but she was my boss all the same and so I got down to work, trying to create some order out of the chaos.

Now that I was settled in one place for the foreseeable future and earning good money, I wrote to my sweetheart back in Aberdeen telling her all about my journeys and that I was in Australia, earning double what I had in Aberdeen. I assured her that I was saving every penny so that I could come home to her all the quicker. I missed her desperately.

On my first day off, I wandered out into the surrounding countryside and once again carved two hearts entwined with our names on a suitable tree. It was my way of keeping her memory fresh in my mind - just a gesture perhaps - but I carved it with love and longing in my heart.

I soon settled into a routine with Sarah and the store. Within a few days I had most of the paperwork in hand, separating it by invoices paid and payable, both incoming and outgoing and also by date. Sales were strictly cash only and I entered all the income from that at the end of each day of trading in a ledger. I also showed her how it was done, so when I moved on, as I inevitably would, she'd have a better idea how to keep things organised if she needed to do it herself. She seemed very pleased with my work and called me her 'miracle worker' but it was no miracle, just basic book-keeping.

My little corner of the storeroom, although comfortable enough, had no luxuries like cooking facilities for instance, so I found a café, just a few doors down from the store where I could have some of my meals. I also kept a few things, like biscuits and cheese in a sealed box, for emergencies. I didn't have to bother so much on Sundays, for reasons which will become obvious. The store was closed every Sunday, not that Sarah was religious or anything but it would have been very much frowned upon for any business to be trading on the, 'Sabbath day.'

One of the little conventions we soon established was that I would eat with Sarah on Sundays. As she said, it was a long day, especially with her being on her own. She loved to cook but it didn't seem worth the bother when she was on her own. So, every Sunday lunchtime, I would climb the forbidden stairway, as I thought of it humorously in my mind, and spend a good portion of the day with Sarah who would feed me whatever wonderful dish she had cooked for the day. Mostly it was a traditional roast, whether chicken, pork, lamb, or beef. It was always cooked to perfection and she was very generous with the helpings. I think she was 'mothering' me because I was so far from home and she had no children of her own. The truth was that she wasn't that much older than I was. I was just past my mid twenties and, as it turned out, she was thirty two or three, a woman in her prime.

Afterwards, we would play a few hands of cards, 'the devil's bible' as she referred to them, but laughing as she said it. Sometimes after lunch or dinner she would read to me, stories from her small library of books. She had a wonderfully soothing voice, low and expressive, which really brought the stories to life. I liked her enormously, her sense of humour was second to none, she was extremely intelligent and well read and far from being the stern, older woman I had first thought her, she became what I considered a good friend and companion.

Sundays became the high point of my week. However, back in the store on Monday mornings she was Mrs Davidson once more and all business. She explained to me that things had to be this way, otherwise rumours would soon start to fly and her reputation and business may well suffer too if people thought there was more than just a working relationship.

'I mean it sounds silly I know,' she said. 'A young man like you, and a dried up old widow like me, but idle tongues gossip, and make up stories to suit themselves, and we can't have that.'

'You're not a dried up old widow,' I protested, quite indignantly. 'You're a beautiful woman, intelligent, and hard working with a lovely subtle sense of humour. They don't know you like I do.'

She smiled at me, and reaching up her hand gently stroked my cheek.

'Well bless you young man for making me feel so much better. It's a long time since anybody has called me beautiful.'

Her voice was earnest, but gentle, with a wistful look on her face.

'Thank you. Now back to work, I'm not paying you to stand about idly, giving the boss undeserved compliments, we have a business to run.'

Her laugh broke the tension and we went about our various tasks for the day.

The following Saturday evening after the store had closed, and I'd had something to eat from the café down the street, I was sitting up in bed, reading a book. I was fully dressed and on top of the covers; there was nowhere comfortable to sit, apart from the bed; when Sarah came into the storeroom. She had some papers in her hand and was checking some of the new stock which had just arrived that morning.

153

'Sorry to bother you,' she said, 'just ignore me while I check this.'

'Can I help you at all,' I asked, getting up from the bed, and laying my book down.

'No, no, don't let me disturb you, carry on reading your book. I'll manage just fine,' she assured me.

Looking across at where my bed was, she spoke again.

'You're going to ruin your eyes, trying to read in that light,' she warned, referring to the candle-light I was reading by.

'Well, they're fine so far but a candle's the best I can do and it's too early to go to bed just yet.' She nodded and smiled and I could see she was thinking.

'Why don't you come up, and I'll make us a cup of tea, and I'll maybe even find some cake or biscuits too?' she offered.

I thought it very kind of her and a splendid idea, and said so, blowing out the candle. Always mindful of the fire hazard, I usually set the candle up in a small enamel bowl to prevent any mishaps. She was carrying a paraffin lamp, which shed a much better light, and with her task finished, I followed her up the stairs.

Her own quarters were feminine and very cosy, not to mention very comfortable too and it wasn't long before she came through from the kitchen to where I was in her parlour with a tray, teapot, cups etc., and poured me tea. Knowing how I liked it, from my previous visits, she added milk and one spoon of sugar.

'There now, help yourself to a biscuit or cake,' she urged, 'make yourself at home.'

Despite the fact that she was my boss, I felt very relaxed in her company.

'It's nice to have someone to talk to, it can get very lonely when you are left to sit on your own night after night,' she explained, smiling.

'I would have thought you would have plenty of friends to keep you company,' I queried.

She thought for a moment, and sighed.

'I did have, and when I was newly widowed they rallied round like you would expect friends to do. But a widow is a single woman and a single woman can be seen as dangerous. Very soon I found myself being excluded from the things my husband and I had been invited to when he was alive. Gradually they all disappeared. Oh, they still talk to me as friendly as ever when they come into the store, or when I see them in the street but that's about it.'

When I became somewhat indignant on her behalf, she smiled indulgently.

'It's okay, I quite understand, they're just afraid that I may try to steal their husbands,' and then she laughed. 'Silly fools, I wouldn't have any of their husbands for all the tea in China.'

The tea, cake and biscuits was lovely and we talked for some time about this and that, about the latest books, politics, and the latest news in the newspapers. As I said, she had a bright and enquiring mind, shrewd and intelligent, with many interests. Eventually the topic came round to my home in Aberdeen. She already knew I had a sweetheart back home, 'in the old country,' as many Australians referred to it, who I would be returning too, and I wasn't planning on settling permanently in Australia.

She asked me all about her and I told her. She smiled wistfully again, a tinge of sadness in her eyes.

'I miss my husband so much too,' she admitted, 'it's a hard and lonely thing to be on your own for so long.'

She gave herself a bit of a shake, and rising from her chair, gathered up the tea things, taking them back to the kitchen. I stood up too, making ready to go back downstairs.

'You're not going already are you?' she said coming to me. 'It's not late, and tomorrow is Sunday after all.'

She looked up into my face. 'Stay awhile, please.'

'I didn't want to outstay my welcome,' I said awkwardly, by way of explanation.

She smiled again, her eyes holding mine, and reached up to stroke my cheek tenderly as she had once before.

'Don't be silly, you could never do that,' she almost whispered as she reached up, and kissed me on the lips.

Surprised at first, I kissed her back, the need in me

156

and my liking and admiration for her overwhelming any reservations I may have had. She was a mature, passionate woman and I was a lonely young man, far from home. We were both swept away in the moment.

Next morning, she rose before I was awake and made breakfast, bringing it to me in bed. She smiled down at me and kissed me again.

'I don't do breakfast in bed very often, but I thought this was a special occasion,' she volunteered by way of an explanation, not that any explanation was required for me.

She came back into bed with me and we both enjoyed our breakfast before doing once again what comes so naturally to new lovers.

Later, as she prepared lunch and I helped her out, we talked over our situation, now that it had developed beyond employer and employee. She was quite anxious that we should keep it secret and I agreed wholeheartedly. We didn't need any gossip, nor petty jealousies amongst the other staff members or customers, so secrecy was going to be the order of the day. We agreed that there must be no touching, or anything out of the ordinary when others were around. I would *not* be moving upstairs. I would continue to sleep in the storeroom to allay any suspicions except when she invited me upstairs. That suited me fine, for to tell the truth, as much as I liked and admired Sarah, yes, and loved her a little too, I felt guilty about my sweetheart back in Aberdeen.

In the next few months we took, and found, great joy in each other's company. She was a delight to be with and it wasn't just the lovemaking, she never ceased to surprise me with the depths of her knowledge. She was my equal and more in most things, our relationship was one of true partners and my feelings for her deepened over the coming months, although this left me very confused. I realised I had grown to love Sarah, despite the six or seven year gap in our ages. Yet there was my own darling girl back home in Aberdeen who I still thought of on a daily basis.

One night, after I'd been with her for almost a year, Sarah asked me what my plans were for the future. To be honest, I just didn't know. She knew I had originally planned to be with her for a year or so at most, before going back home to Scotland. Our unexpected love affair had changed things dramatically.

'I know you still think of her and you keep her photo beside your bed, I mean the bed in the storeroom,' she said with a wicked grin, since I now spent a lot of nights in her bed. I always rose in the early hours to return to my storeroom bed. We didn't want the other workers to see me coming downstairs in the morning.

'Yes, I do think of her, I'll be honest, but I'm so happy here with you too. I'm very confused I have to admit. If it wasn't for her, I'd stay here with you and never think of leaving, and I know I'd be very happy being with you.' I really was confused about the issue – torn one way and another.

'God knows, I don't want to lose you,' she said sorrowfully, 'you must know I love you too?'

I nodded and looked at her. She wasn't one given to crying but I could see her eyes had filled up, as had my own. It was a very tense and emotional moment and we clung to each other for solace.

'You must leave as soon as possible,' she declared, suddenly taking charge. 'Go home, see her again, and decide. I can't live with the uncertainty. I desperately want you to stay with me, but you're not truly mine until this is fixed, and I want you to be mine and mine alone, with no ifs and buts.'

With the decision made and a long tear stained parting behind me, I soon found myself doing the rounds of shipping agents at Sydney harbour looking for a berth on a ship bound for home. The best I could find was one bound for South Africa, so I signed up, hoping that I could find one from there to home'

Life on board ship was much the same as it had been on my previous two spells, basically working and sleeping, keeping myself to myself. I had mixed feelings, happy in some ways, but filled with trepidation for my journey home, and desperately missing Sarah too. I would look at my watch, and try to work out the time difference and think what she'd be doing back in Teetulpa.

I sent her a letter after I was discharged in Cape Town, telling her that I was thinking of her and missing her so much, and I was.

Determined to see a little of the country, after all, it's not every day that you land on the great continent of Africa, I decided to explore a little, before finding another ship for the last leg of my journey home. I found myself on a train, heading for the interior, to the Transvaal to be precise. I hadn't a clue what was there but I knew there had been a gold rush there a few years previously. I just liked the name, it sounded exotic, so I followed my instincts and went there.

I met some nice people of Dutch origin who were very hospitable and explored the countryside with the help of a native guide for a couple of days. The country teemed with wildlife and I saw many different types of antelope, giraffe, rhino, elephants, and of course lions, who seemed to enjoy a very lazy lifestyle, sleeping under shady trees for most of the time. I found a suitable tree, without the accompanying lions under it thankfully and once again carved the name of my sweetheart on the bark, with the two heart entwined, although by now I wasn't quite so certain about my feelings, but it had become a ritual for me and I carried it on.

Back in Cape Town, it wasn't long before I found a ship heading for the Port of London and signed up for the voyage home. Once again crossing the equator, the ceremonies for

King Neptune took place but since I had obviously been subjected to the nonsense before, I managed to avoid it. There was little of note about the voyage, apart from some bad weather at the Bay of Biscay. We soon sailed through that and were on the homeward stretch, docking in the Port of London very soon afterwards.

Now that I was almost home, I began to look forward to seeing my family, friends and sweetheart again. I caught the overnight train from London and was back home in Aberdeen by mid-morning. It was three years since I had left, and my mother wept for joy to see me again. Even my dad had tears in his eyes and gave me a welcome hug, something he hadn't done since I was a little boy. We're an undemonstrative lot at times, we Aberdonian's, but the love is there, just below the surface all the same.

My mother's first instinct was to feed me and so the table was set for lunch, my brother and sister being sent for by my dad to welcome me home. We all sat down, with their families and children. It felt almost like Christmas when we were children, with us all together again. It was a lovely warm and comforting feeling being back in the bosom of my family once more.

During the course of the meal, I thought it a bit strange that nobody had mentioned Katie, so I asked why.

'Has onnybody seen my Katie lately, is she in good health, is she okay?'

I could tell by the way they passed furtive looks at each other in an embarrassed silence that something was wrong.

'Is somebody gan tae tell me then?' I asked, with a sinking feeling in my stomach.

It was my mother who gave me the bad news.

'I'm sorry tae tell ye son, she didna wait for ye like she promised. She took up wi somebody else, and as far as I hear, she's getting' merriet in a month or twa.'

I sat there stunned, everybody else had gone silent, looking at me. My emotions were all over the place. I said nothing after that and ate my lunch. After all my dear mother had gone to all the bother of preparing it. I thought it would have been disrespectful to her and the food not to eat it and enjoy it. Gradually things returned to normal at the table, or as near normal as possible after such bad news.

I went round to Katie's house after lunchtime, determined to hear it from her own mouth, and knocked on the door.

Her mother answered and looked totally shocked, and then dismayed.

'She's nae in, I dinna ken far she is,' she blurted out, and then I heard Katie shout from upstairs.

'Who is it mum?' she called.

'Ye'd better come doon, it's somebody for you,' her mother said, and walked away with a resigned look on her face, leaving the door open.

I heard Katie tripping down the stairs and when she turned at the bottom to come to the door, she saw me and stopped dead in her tracks.

'Oh no, it canna be, what are you deein here?' she said, face white with shock.

That reaction answered any questions I may have had. She should have thrown herself into my arms, the fact that she didn't told me all.

'So it's true then?' I stated. 'Ye didna wait for me and yer merryin' anither man.'

Her mouth opened as if to say something but nothing came out. I turned and left, I heard her call my name when I was half way down the street but it was too late by then.

To say I was upset would be putting it mildly. I mourned for Katie, I grieved for her loss but after a week or two of moping about, I made a firm decision. I would leave Aberdeen and I would not return. Instead I would go to Australia and Sarah and make a new life there, or rather, take up where I left off, if she would have me after all this carry on. I had been very happy with Sarah. I loved her and after the hurt of finding that Katie had broken her promise to me, I would go to Sarah and let things develop as they may.

I told my family I was returning to Australia, that I had a good job there earning twice what I was making in Aberdeen and now that Katie had let me down, my future prospects lay in Australia. I never mentioned Sarah to them, they didn't need to know. I visited my bank to check on my assets, which were fairly sizeable after my enhanced earning capacity with the Hudson's Bay Company, my seaman's earnings, and my earnings from working with Sarah.

I had lived a very frugal existence and saved virtually all of my pay for the time I was away. I paid a sizeable sum into my parent's bank account as a gift to make their impending old age a little more comfortable, a few hundred each to my brother and sister. After I had made my gifts I still had a sizeable sum, so I was quite content with myself, and while I regretted the fact that I may never see my family again, I had resolved to make a new life for myself on the other side of the world.

I had intended to send a note to Katie, asking to meet her before leaving, but in the end I thought better of it. What good would it do? She had made her choice. Instead, I left a letter for my brother to send to her after I'd left. I just said that by the time she got the letter, I'd be on my way back to Australia, and I hoped she'd be very happy, and I enclosed her photo and that was that.

I also wrote a letter to Sarah, letting her know that I was on my way home to her, for I now thought of Sarah as my, 'home.'

A couple of weeks later I was on my way to London, having secured a berth on a merchant ship to Australia.

Within the month I was landing at Sydney harbour. The next day I walked through the door of Sarah's store into the arms of my love. She hugged me and kissed me unashamedly in front of everyone in the store.

'What happened to secrecy and discretion?' I asked her a little later that evening.

'Oh bugger that,' she laughed, 'I was just so glad to see you, I wanted to shout it out on the main street, and for the whole world to know you were back and everything was right again.'

She launched herself back into my arms again.

'Promise you won't leave me again,' she whispered in my ear. It wasn't a hard promise to make.

'I suppose now that you've announced it to the world, your reputation is shot to bits,' I concluded.

She shrugged her shoulders, and made a funny face, obviously not caring at all.

'Does this mean I have to make an, "honest," woman of you now?' I teased.

Her face broke into a huge grin.

'Are you saying what I think you're saying?' she asked, smiling at me again.

'That's exactly what I'm saying my darling Sarah. Will you do me the honour of being my wife?'

She came into my arms again, eye to eye, her blue eyes sparkling with love and happiness.

'Oh yes my darling boy, yes,' she answered, kissing me again.

She started laughing, and when I asked her why, it was ages before she could speak without laughing again.

'I'm so glad you asked me to marry you, because, well... maybe you'd better sit down.'

I did as she asked, uncomprehending, but looking at her expectantly.

'Yes?' I asked, 'well... what?' She smiled at me once more.

'You're going to be a daddy.'

I sat there dumbfounded, I'm pretty sure my mouth was open in astonishment and I was doing a fairly convincing impression of a hungry guppy fish. She looked at me, maybe not just quite sure how I was taking the news but it was wonderful news to me, a day of delights. I jumped to my feet and took her in my arms again.

'Sarah, you wonderful, wonderful woman. I'm so happy. We'll need to get married straight away then.'

She nodded her head, and we did.

We were safely delivered of a beautiful baby girl, Emily and a couple of years later, a son, Thomas, named after my father. We are blissfully happy, oh sure we argue from time to time, but making up is always so much fun, don't you think so?

18. THE ONCOMING LIGHT

This is quite a short story and rather than call it a ghost story, for I saw no ghost, I prefer to call it, 'unexplained.' It happened back in the late spring of 1963. I was fifteen years old at the time and had just left school a few months previously.

As soon as I left school at Christmas, in the winter of 1962/3, my mother made the decision that we would leave the home where I'd been brought up, on a council estate in Aberdeen, and go and stay with my grandparents Davy and Jean Stewart just outside Banchory, until she had saved enough money for a deposit to buy a house or a flat, rather than rent one from the council as we were doing.

My Granny and Grandad lived in a small farm, about sixteen acres or slightly bigger, just off the Raemoir Road on the outskirts of Banchory, which is almost twenty miles from Aberdeen. It was situated on the left side of Raemoir Road, just across from where the garden centre is now, a few hundred yards further along the road leading out of Banchory, where the road dips down and before it starts to climb out of the hollow again. The farm had the inviting name of 'Rotten Moss' which makes me smile to this day every time I drive past where it was located. The land was sold for private housing a few years after my grandparents passed away in the 1970's and a fair number of very large 'exclusive' houses were built on it. So it amuses me that these 'posh' houses are built on 'Rotten Moss.' If only they knew. They maybe will now, if any of them ever read this story.

Following the move to Banchory with my mother and my brother, it would be something of an understatement to say I was most upset. Here I was, a 15 year old city boy, uprooted from everything I'd ever known, set down in the middle of the country, with nothing to do and nowhere to go. In Aberdeen, I had loads of friends from school - people I'd grown up with - and being in the city, more things to do as well. Sometimes at night I'd look out of the skylight window of the farmhouse bedroom towards Aberdeen where I could see the lights of the city reflected on the clouds and desperately long to be there. I never got used to living in the country. Although it has to be said in all fairness, I had lots of cousins and relatives in the area. But most of my cousins were slightly older, or younger and lived a few miles from the farm. I spent a lot of time on my own reading, but then I always had.

However, looking back, I was lucky in some ways, because most of my mother's business dealings were in Aberdeen, which meant that two or three times a week, I would visit the city with her, meet with Jim, my best friend from school, and go to the cinema or such like. Afterwards I'd meet up with my mother at my aunt's house and maybe have a cup of tea and a 'news' as we called it. Just long rambling conversations about various topics, other family members, music, or the state of the country, whatever came to mind. It was an early night if we left my aunt's house before 11pm to set out for Banchory.

Being brought up in the Banchory area, my mother and her family rarely drove into Aberdeen on the usual route, the North Deeside road, through the small villages of Cults and Culter but preferred what we called the 'back road' which was the road that led out of Aberdeen past Kingswells, Garlogie and Cullerlie then into Banchory on the aforementioned Raemoir Road. So, the scene was set. It was late at night, almost midnight, on a dark and lonely country road.

It was a clear night, no fog, mist or rain, as my mother drove us back to Banchory. We were chatting occasionally but mostly just silent. We both knew the road well, having journeyed on it many, many times before. We came to where there was a short straight, a mile or two before Cullerlie, with an old farmhouse on the right hand side of the road. Up ahead there was an 'S' bend, which veered to the left before snaking up round the crest of the hill as it turned to the right. Just as we came opposite the farm house, I saw a light come round the crest of the hill heading down towards us. It seemed very high and almost at our side of the road; and I called out to my mother in alarm.

'You'll need to pull mair ower tae this side o' the road, that thing's gaen tae hit us.'

My mother assured me that she was as close to the edge as she could get but she braked, slowed down and then suddenly the light was gone, it just wasn't there anymore. There was nowhere for any vehicle to turn off, just the road in front of us, it hadn't passed us, so where was it? My mother didn't stop the car. We just drove on to Banchory, speculating as to what happened on the rest of the journey.

My granny and grandad were still up when we got back. We've never been early to bed type people and grandad asked us if we'd had a good night.

'Aye, it was just fine, but an affa queer thing happened on the wye hame,' my mother said, and then she told my grandfather about what we'd seen, the light coming towards us and what had happened.

He looked at her.

'Ye've gotten a warnin' lassie,' he said, shaking his head. 'Aye, ye've gotten a warnin' and it's nae gaen tae be good news.'

'Ach, it was jist a light da, I'm sure it's nae onnything bad,' my mother protested, not sounding very sure about it. My grandad shook his head again.

'I'm sorry Maggie,' he warned, 'but yer gaen tae get bad news and it will be news o' a death in the family. It was a warnin' licht, jist you wait and see.'

He walked away, calling on his wee dog, Flossie as he went outside to check the out-buildings were locked and secure for the night before going to bed.

Nothing was said about what happened the next day, and to tell the truth we had almost forgotten it until the following week, when once again we were on our way home late, well after 11pm, drawing closer to midnight.

'I winder if we'll see that queer licht again Ma,' I said as we drew closer, just a mile or two from the place where we'd seen it the previous week.

'Nah,' my mother said quietly, 'there must be some fools, scaldie laddies, wee bammie ruchies, acting the goat, playing tricks, or... or something, aye that's whit it will be,' she finished lamely, sounding as if she was trying to convince herself and me.

Looking back, I can see she was trying to protect me and assure me in case I was scared but it had happened so quickly the last time, I'd had no time to be frightened.

As we approached the same bit of the road, we were looking for it to appear again and we weren't to be disappointed. Suddenly it was there, sweeping round the bend towards us, a high, bright light, like a lorry.

'Here it comes again ma,' I said quietly.

'Aye, I see it,' she replied, slowing down a wee bit in case this time it was a real lorry. But just like the time before, it simply vanished before it reached us.

'God bless us,' she said loudly, like a wee prayer as she drove on.

'That's something that's nae richt. My father wis richt, it *is* a warning licht.'

There was nothing much to say after that and we drove home in silence.

'Did ye see the licht again Maggie?' was the first thing my grandad said as we went into the living room.

'Aye da, she replied, 'it was exactly the same licht, and it came tae us at the very same spot as before.'

She looked worried and once again my grandad voiced his opinion that it was a warning light and we'd get bad news very soon. The next few times we went into Aberdeen, we came home by the North Deeside Road and saw nothing. But two or three weeks later we were coming home and I think my mother was so used to driving home on the 'back road' that I think she took it automatically without thinking about it, which was fine by me, as I'd never been frightened by the appearance of the light in the first place. Again, like the other nights we'd seen the light, it was a clear, dry night, no rain or mist to obscure the vision. As we approached the stretch of road we'd come to dread, we speculated as to whether we'd see something tonight. Of course we were hoping to see nothing at all.

'Oh ma, ma,' I said, 'here it comes, here it comes again.'

It was the same thing once more, a bright, bright light, high up off the road, like a lorry headlight, bearing down, hurtling towards us, and then gone. Vanished completely. No vehicle ever passed us and, as I said before, there was nowhere for it to go, no other side road, or an opening into a field where it could have swung off the road. It was a complete mystery, and remains so to this day. If I'm out on that road, coming home late at night, I still approach that particular stretch of the road with a sense of trepidation but I have never seen anything.

My grandfather repeated his opinion when we got home, that it was a warning light, adding 'That's three times ye've seen it. Ye winna see it again, ye've gotten yer warning noo.' He was right; we never saw the light again and we travelled in and out of Aberdeen on that road for nearly a year, while we lived in Banchory, so I suppose my auld grandfather was right about that.

Now, I know you're all wondering if the oncoming light really was a warning about a death in the family. The simple answer is, I don't know and, to tell the truth, what happened could have been an unfortunate coincidence. Terrible tragedy did strike the family about a month or two later. One of my cousins was killed in a road accident. He was driving a lorry at the time. A young man in his twenties, with his whole life in front of him, taken far too soon. Much loved by all who knew him, and sadly missed.

19. THE CASTLE

When I was offered the chance to transfer from the main office of the firm I worked for and take charge of the smaller branch in Castleton, I have to admit I was rather reluctant to move at first. After weighing my options up however, I finally decided the opportunity was just too good to miss, although moving from the city to such a small town was a complete change for me.

A medieval castle dominated the town; a picturesque and massive ruin on the hilltop; which gave the place its name and that same name was writ large in the street names and shops of the old town. The Castle Bakery, the Castle Newsagents, the Castle Shoeshop, and so on. I settled in quickly and found a temporary flat until something better came along. Without even looking for romance, I met a lovely girl called Katie. I'd dated her a couple of times in the first two weeks and we seemed to get on really well. She was good company, light hearted and flirtatious, with a great sense of humour. It all seemed to be going smoothly, but given my naturally pessimistic Scottish nature, a bit too smoothly I suspected. The light at the end of *my* tunnel nearly always proved to be a train coming in the opposite direction.

I called her again, eager to arrange another date, and she suggested we meet at the castle. And so it was that I found myself trudging up the hill towards the ruins on

Saturday afternoon. It was a nice enough day but when I reached the castle ruins the wind was fairly whistling round the crumbling walls and after a few minutes I was feeling the cold. However, she was worth a wee bit of discomfort I thought, and so I waited, and waited. Eventually, twenty minutes past the agreed time, I tried to call her on my mobile phone but there was no signal. I waited some more, getting colder by the minute but after another twenty minutes I reluctantly decided that she'd stood me up. Puzzled and decidedly angry, I made my way down the hill, back to my flat. I heard nothing more from her that weekend and although I liked her enormously, that old Scottish pessimism kicked in and I told myself she'd gone, 'off,' me, and that was the end of that.

After work on Monday I was in the supermarket doing some food shopping when I saw her at the other side of the freezer section. At first I decided to ignore her; after all, a man has to have some pride, I thought. She studiously avoided me too which somehow angered me even more. After all, I was the injured party, I reasoned and she might at least have the decency to apologise. I took the proverbial bull by the horns but in her case it was a cow, I thought.

'Well… thanks for standing me up on Saturday,' I said, just to let her know she wasn't getting off with it.

'What? Me, stand you up? I waited for over an hour and you never came. I was really upset,' she retaliated, a hint of tears in her eyes.

'Rubbish, I was there, and there was no sign of you. I waited nearly an hour and I was bloody frozen into the bargain,' I complained. 'I thought you were something special. I just can't understand why you would arrange to meet me and leave me standing on top of that damned hill all afternoon,' I said, exaggerating my ordeal for better effect, and pointing in the vague direction of the castle.

She looked at me, a puzzled look on her face at first, saying nothing and then she started to laugh.

'I don't see what's funny about that,' I said, with obvious annoyance in my voice.

'Oh my god... but, don't you see, it *is* quite funny actually?' she said laughing again. 'When I said I'd meet you at, "The Castle," I meant the pub just off the high street in Castle Road. You poor darling, I'd forgotten you're new here. I'm so sorry,' she said, reaching up and kissing my cheek. I felt rather foolish, but much happier.

'I've been utterly miserable all weekend,' I admitted.

'Me too,' she said giving me a consoling hug, adding, 'can we start again?'

I readily agreed and after finishing our shopping we walked round the corner where she introduced me to, 'The Castle' a warm and welcoming pub, which like her, I found much to my liking. I grew to love Katie and Castleton, and over the years we've turned down numerous chances to move on to 'better' and more lucrative positions within the company. Fifteen years have passed since that memorable day. Katie and I still have the occasional drink at 'The Castle' but not quite so often as we used to. Finding baby sitters for our three children can be difficult.

20. THE PERFUME JAR

Once upon a time, a long, long time ago, there lived a family of little people. Now when I say little people, I don't mean just naturally wee folk, I mean magical beings, sometimes called Brownies, but known locally as 'Broonies' for they lived in Scotland and as such were even more troublesome than their distant relatives in faraway England.

They were up to every kind of tricks; turning milk black and sour, unscrewing the lavvy seats so folk fell backwards into the poop when they sat doon, knocking at the door, and rinnin awa', or even tying a rope roon the door knob and tying the other end tae a drain-pipe, or a boulder, then putting a big grassy sod on the lum, so the smoke fae the fire would go back intae the room and nip yer eyes, and ye couldna get oot, for they'd tied the door knob tae a drain pipe.

Well this family o' broonies lived on the estate of a great Laird, under a great and magical oak tree. There was a tunnel under the mighty roots of this huge and ancient tree, and it led doon tae a great door, and the entrance tae the land o' the broonies. This Laird, a maist disagreeable man it has tae be said, was a man wha widna gie ye a drink o watter if ye were dying and takin yer last gasp. He thocht it was time tae get rid o the broonies for once and for all. So he ordered some o' his woodsmen tae get their saws and axes ready, and follow him tae the edge of the great wids whaur the oak tree grew.

When the woodmen saw the tree he wanted tae cut doon they turned as white as ghosts and protested that they couldna cut doon the magic oak tree.

'Oh naw Laird, ye canna cut doon the Magic Oak, for ye'll never hae good luck in this world or the next. Dinna mak us cut it doon. We'll be cursed forever, and so will oor femilys,' they all said.

'Rubbish,' the Laird screamed at them flying intae a rage as usual, 'ye'll cut it doon, or ye can aw get aff o' my estate and tak yer rotten stinky femilys wi ye, ye'll nae get anither job onnyplace, for I'll tell the other land owners yer a bunch o' lazy, scabby, good for nithing troublemakers.'

They hung their heids in shame as the Laird insulted them but they could dae nithing, for this was the Laird, the man who paid their wages. Without his money and their jobs, their bairns wid starve and die.

At last, one woodsman, a bit braver, or a bit mair stupid - naebody wis ever quite sure which - stepped forward. The Laird pointed to the tree.

'Do your job man, ye'll be well rewarded,' he ordered.

So reluctantly the woodsman stepped up closer to the tree, looked at the Laird, who nodded and smiled an evil, wicked smile.

'Carry on man, carry on,' he urged.

So the woodsman reluctantly swung his axe, the sharp blade heading for the ancient bark of the tree.

'Clang!!!! Booooing!!,' an almighty sound like all the bells of hell ringing at once came from the tree. There was not one scratch on the tree bark but the sound of the bells had been so loud it had blown all the woodsmen off their feet.

The Lairds horse reared up on its hind legs and the Laird was thrown off to land in a very big and very prickly thorn bush. The horse was so feart, it bolted and ran awa, leaving the Laird tae walk hame.

Now, the maist horrible screams of rage and fury could be heard from under the tree and, within seconds, broonies by the dozen surged out from under the tree, armed to the teeth, ready to dae battle. The leader of the broonies, a most wise, clever and wily man, saw the laird lying in the thorn bush. He gave orders for the Laird to be helped to his feet at once.

'Och, it's just yourself is it Laird? What can we do for you?' he inquired, smiling as if nothing had happened.

The Laird of course was furious, so furious he could hardly speak but he raged and ranted until his face was absolutely crimson and then turned a maist attractive shade o' purple with rage.

'Do for me, do for me..? You can get off my land or I'll burn you out,' he screamed. 'Aye you and a' the other little people and faery folk in the woods. You're a damned nuisance, all of you, stealing, causing damage, leaving dirt everywhere. I've had enough, you're nae use to onnybody, a waste of space. GET OFF MY LAND!!' He screamed.

Now, as had been said, the leader of the broonies was a most wise, clever and wily man, so remained absolutely calm in the face of this tirade.

'Ah well now my dear Laird,' he said softly, 'we've lived here for hundreds of years, lang before you, or even your ancestors came here. We were granted these woods by your very first ancestor, who also mistakenly thocht he owned everything, until he saw the error of his ways, and we have the legal papers to prove it.'

'I don't care,' screamed the Laird, 'when I burn you out, the legal papers will burn as weel and then you canna prove a thing,' and he laughed, a wicked, evil laugh.

'Oh come now your Lairdship, we have oor uses. Ye ken fine we mak the best perfume in the land and the King himself loves it's scent. And ye ken that the King has almost no sense of smell, yet oor perfume is so good he can smell it no bother and loves us for it. What wid he say if you killed us, the folk that mak the only thing he can smell?'

The Laird had forgotten this of course but now he thought of a great way to catch the King's favour.

'Very well,' he said at last, 'The King is going to make a visit to my estate here in the late summer. If I had a jar of your best perfume to present to him as a gift, I'm sure he would be pleased and maybe make me the Prime Minister, second only to himself in importance as ruler of the Kingdom.' He smiled wickedly.

'Who knows,' he thought, 'if the King should happen to die, I may well become King after him.'

But he was thinking out loud, not realising everybody could hear his treacherous plans. When he had finished plotting badness, he turned tae the broonies.

'I'll hae the jar I want filled with perfume delivered to you richt awa' – you have a month to fill it. If nae,' he made a gesture with his finger across his throat, 'heids will roll.'

Now, the broonies were famous for their perfume. They collected wild flowers of every type from the meadows and the woods, and the concentrated smell of their perfume was almost magical in its effect. They brewed it deep, doon in the earth and even a wee jar meant hours and hours of hard work for them. Imagine then their dismay when the jar the Laird wanted filled arrived on the back of a horse and cart. They all gathered round in disbelief.

'That jar must be seven feet high if it's an inch,' one raged.

'How are we ever going to fill that?' they moaned.

'A man could fa' into that jar and droon, it's so big,' one exclaimed.

And the leader of the broonies, on hearing this, set a

182

plan in motion.

Gathering the elders of the clan around him, he laid his plan before them. Filling the jar with perfume was an impossible task. Even the wonderfully industrious broonies kent they would never manage to fill it with their special perfume, so just for the Laird, they would fill it with something else. Something that smelled just as strongly as their perfume.

When at last the jar was filled, they left it to mature and grow even stronger, like a ripe cheese, until the Laird sent them an urgent message.

'The King will be here in a few days. I hope you have filled the jar, otherwise heids will roll,' he threated again.

The leader of the broonies, unworried by his threats, sent him a message the very same day telling him the jar was as full as it needed to be, but not all the way to the top, because it needed to have some 'breathing space' contact with the air to smell its best.

In the meantime, he added, they had sealed the jar with a heavy lid to stop the perfume evaporating. The Laird, as nasty as ever, ripped up the letter and threw it in the fire, laughing tae himself, muttering, 'Heids will roll, heids will roll.' He had nae intention of keeping his word.

The next day the broonies got the huge jar ready, and loaded it aboard the horse and cart.

'Michty me, it must weigh a ton, or even mair,' groaned

the sweating broonies, as they struggled with the jar, but they finally managed to get it into the cart, and tied doon so it didna fa' aff the back on its way up to the Lairds castle.

The road was rough, and they could hear the contents o' the jar splooshing, slopping, and stirring aboot inside.

'That will help to keep the aroma nice and strong,' they laughed to themselves.

Finally they arrived at the castle and the Laird ordered them to take the jar intae the great hall, whaur the feast in honour of the king was going to be held.

'Careful, careful,' he shouted, disagreeable as ever, 'if ye spill even one drop, heids will roll, heids will roll, I warn ye.'

The Laird wanted the broonies to unseal the jar but the leader of the broonies, warned against it.

'Only the king may open the jar. It has a spell of protection placed upon it and if anybody except the king unseals the jar, I won't be held responsible for what happens to them,' he warned menacingly.

'What would happen if somebody wis tae open it other than the king,' he asked, sleekitly?

'Weel noo,' said the leader o' the broonies, 'ye've heard o' a spell, that can gie ye warts on yer face?' he asked.

The Laird nodded his heid warily.

'Aye, aye, I've heard o' that, but what's tae stop me ordering one of my servants tae open it?' he said, cleverly as he thocht.

'Weel ye could,' the broonies headman said, 'but this is a very finely devised spell. Its effect will fall on those *responsible* for the unsealing of the jar. So, if you ordered a servant to open it, it would still be you, and nae the servant wha wid suffer the consequences.'

The wicked laird harrumphed his displeasure.

'Okay, I suppose it nae worth the bother o' getting a face full o' warts, just for a sniff o' perfume,' he moaned.

'Och dear me Laird, ye widna get warts on *your* face,' the broonies leader said and he smiled, 'nithing as nice as that, na, na, ye wid jist turn intae one o' the warts on the face o' somebody else.'

The Laird glowered at him, and vowed vengeance tae himself, thinking how delighted and happy he wid be tae see the broonie leader's heid roll doon the brae like an Easter egg.

The next day all of the castle was hustle and bustle as the Laird's downtrodden servants, who had already been forced to work half the night, set about laying the great tables with umpteen glasses for the many fine wines tae accompany the feast. So many different knives, forks, and spoons for the many courses they were preparing in the kitchen, where the kitchen servants and cooks worked in the heat of the huge roasting fires until the sweat was fair blinnin' them. They kent that after the feast, they'd be up half the night washing and scrubbing all the pots, pans, glasses, dishes and cutlery that had been used during the course of the great feast. After that they'd have to wash and launder all the spotless white linen tablecloths and napkins, and hae them ready for breakfast next morning, for the king and his huge following of Lairds and Ladies were staying overnight, and when they left, the servants would have to wash and launder all those sheets and pillowcases too. It was an exhausting business being a servant for the great Laird, and the wages he paid were barely enough to keep them from starving.

An hour or so later a rider galloped into the castle courtyard and announced that the King would be with them very soon. A great fanfare of trumpets announced his arrival.

'Toot toot ta root, toot ta toot ta tat tooooo!' blared the trumpets. Everybody cheered as the King arrived, for he was a most popular king and was well liked by his subjects. The Laird smiled and welcomed the king to his castle but the King, if the truth be told, had no liking for the greasy, slimy manners of the Laird. He knew the Laird wanted to be king himself and would stab him in the back if he got half a chance. But politics dictated that he should pretend he liked the Laird until such times as he had some excuse to get rid of him.

One by one, as the great and good paraded through the castle drawing everybody's attention, a select band of broonies sneaked into and infiltrated the castle, blending into the back ground, pretending to be servants and attendants. They were there for one thing only; to make sure their plan went as they intended, with the help o' a wee bit o' magic.

The feast went very well. The King declared the food delicious and most excellent and the Laird was fair beaming with delight as the King heaped praise on his efforts. The jugglers and acrobats, singers and musicians kept everybody amused and delighted between courses and, all in all, the whole feast was going wonderfully well. It was at this point the Laird stood up to make a speech praising the wisdom and popularity of such a great King.

The King beamed and smiled, falsely of course, for he kent the Laird was lying and meant not one single word of what he was saying. However, be that as it may, the Laird announced that he had a most wondrous gift for his Majesty, and unveiled the great jar, explaining that he had gone to great difficulty and spared no expense, which was true, he had spared no expense at all to obtain this wonderful gift for his majesty. Finally adding,

'It is a most wondrous perfume your majesty, and every time your subjects smell it, they will think of you, and know you are close by.'

Of course, the jar being seven feet high, a step ladder was needed so the king could reach the lid and unseal the jar. The broonies had stolen every ladder in the castle earlier that day and left only one. It was the most rickety, ramshackle ladder anybody had ever seen. It creaked and squeaked as his majesty climbed higher, shaking and shuddering with each rung stepped upon. The King was worried that it may collapse but being the king, and a very brave man, he climbed higher until at last he could reach the sealed lid. Everybody below waited expectantly as the king began to unscrew the huge lid. As he unscrewed it, the ladder creaked and groaned with every movement. Finally the lid came loose and was handed down to an attendant.

The smell that emanated from the jar quickly filled the great hall and people looked at each other in horror, some turning a most attractive shade of green, which is fine if you're a shrub, or a herbaceous border but not an attractive skin colour. The smile vanished from the face of the laird and, to add to his misery, one of the queen's ladies in waiting, sickened by the stench, vomited over his shoes.

The King of course, having almost no sense of smell, hadn't noticed the horrified faces of everybody else in the hall. He leaned over the jar to get a better sense of the aroma. This was what the broonies were waiting for and as one they sent and directed their spells at the ladder the king was standing precariously on. The ladder trembled even more, shuddered, and suddenly gave way, tipping the King, head over heels into the jar, and into the, 'perfume.' Only, it wasn't perfume... it was the accumulated pee and poo of the broonies, and it was particularly smelly, because for many days the leader of the broonies had instructed them to eat nothing but fried onions, hard boiled eggs, and kippers.

The King very nearly drowned in the muck but was rescued by the broonies who had, 'miraculously,' found new and very stable ladders, which they climbed up and quickly rescued the King from the jar.

The King stood on the floor of the hall, dripping brown, slimy poo from his once rich and beautiful clothing, his beard, straggly and smelly. Even he could smell it now, and as the first shock wore off, his anger grew and grew until he was absolutely furious. Always the King and statesman, he knew how to turn any situation to his advantage. Quickly controlling his anger, he realised he now had the opportunity and the perfect excuse he needed to rid himself of the wicked Laird.

'Arrest that man,' he screamed, pointing at the Laird, 'arrest him now. This is the worst treason ever heard of, trying to drown me in poo, it's outrageous,' and the Laird was dragged away, kicking and screaming, greeting like a wee bairn.

Justice was swift and merciless in those days long ago, and before tea-time that very evening the Laird's ain words came back to haunt him. His favourite threat, 'heids will roll,' came all too true, but it was *his* heid that rolled, as the King's High Executioner lifted his mighty axe, and with one swift and terrible blow, chopped off the head of the slimy, cruel, and horrible Laird.

As a measure of thanks for helping him out of the jar, and saving him from drowning, the King granted the rights tae the broonies for all eternity, to live on the estate and not be threatened or disturbed in any way. A carefully penned parchment, decorated in beautiful colours with the King's very own coat-of-arms and signature duly arrived, in a rich golden frame. It was hung in the hall of the broonies deep in the earth.

The new Laird, aware of and very happy with the broonies living on his estate, never bothered them and indeed always tipped his hat in respect when he met with any of them when hunting in the woods. Nobody at court ever thought to ask where the Laird had gotten the jar full of stinky poo but the Laird's servants all knew and the woodsmen too. But nobody had liked the Laird and the country folk knew how to keep a secret. They just smiled, and said nothing.

21. THE GROUND SHE WALKS UPON

I remember the first time I saw her, but then, how could I ever forget? She came into my life and in an instant everything changed, and would never be the same again. That's how profound her influence was. I hadn't been looking for someone, not a bit of it, I was just getting on with living, trying to enjoy life as a student, little realising how empty it all really was. Then our paths crossed and she brought everything good into my life, things that I hadn't even imagined before her.

I had gone to University as usual, grudgingly it has to be said, for it was a cold morning and I had struggled to get out of bed. It was one of those days when the alarm clock goes off and it's still dark outside and you feel like turning over, pulling the bedclothes over your head and saying, 'sod it,' to the world. However, I lay there for five minutes thinking about it, then got up, as I said before, very grudgingl. But once up and on the move I quickly got myself ready, had some breakfast and off I went. I sometimes wonder what would have happened if I had decided not to get out of bed that fateful day, just turned over as I was tempted to do and gone back to sleep. Perhaps we were destined to meet anyway, or perhaps my life would have taken an entirely different course, who knows?

My first lecture of the day was for 10am, in the New

Kings lecture theatre, in Aberdeen University. For those of you who don't know the Aberdeen University campus, Kings College is situated in a part of Aberdeen know as, 'Old Aberdeen,' where the university was founded by Bishop William Elphinstone, in 1495, and named after the King Of Scots, James the 4th. New Kings is adjacent to the original part of the college and was built in 1913 to blend in harmoniously with the older buildings, which it does very successfully.

The main lecture theatres in New King's are quite big, holding well over a hundred students at a time, which maybe explains why I'd managed to get half-way through the term without seeing her before. But believe me, once I saw her, that was it. She just appealed to me in every way, her looks initially of course, but later I was to discover more about her which completely reinforced my initial impression.

From the moment I saw her, I couldn't take my eyes off her and eventually she noticed me looking. I smiled at her and she smiled shyly back – bloody hell, she was even better looking when she smiled, I remember thinking. Which is nonsense of course, but I was smitten already and that's how it felt to me. Throughout the lecture our eyes kept meeting and we both kept smiling and I began thinking maybe she liked me too. I haven't a clue to this day what that lecture was about. I could only think of her – she filled my mind and my vision to the exclusion of everything else. I was determined not to lose her in the crush when the lecture was over.

At the end of a lecture, students are inclined to get out quickly, almost as if the place was on fire. I knew it would be easy for us to become separated in the rush, which is another reason why I kept my eyes on her and didn't hear the lecture at all. So, as the lecture was coming to a close, I was kind of 'edgy' and was out of my seat like a greyhound out of the trap when the lecturer called a halt to the proceedings.

As we all filed out, I was right behind her, exactly where I wanted to be, my heart beating with excitement like a very fast drum. I followed her all the way down the stairs, getting closer until, as we went through the main doors out into the cold, she noticed me right behind her. She turned to me and gave me that lovely smile again. I wanted to say something witty, something profound, something impressive, but I struggled to get anything out at all. I just couldn't find the words. My brain had turned to mush at the brightness of her smile. She appeared amused at my discomfiture, her smile never wavered until at last I finally managed to blurt out the most crass and stupid thing possible.

'Y... y... you're lovely,' I stuttered idiotically.

She laughed and I must have looked a little embarrassed and crestfallen.

'Thank you so very much,' was all she said, but making it obvious that she approved, still smiling, her voice was

193

every bit as lovely as the rest of her.

Somehow I found myself walking along next to her. She asked my name and I told her and then she told me hers. As we walked along she slipped her hand into mine.

'It's okay,' she reassured me, 'I like you too.'

Well that was it, and over the next few days and weeks we became inseparable.

I thought I had been in love a couple of times before I met her but she soon showed me that I'd been mistaken. Not in any obvious way, there was no need for her to go out of her way to make herself adorable, just being herself, being the warm, outgoing and considerate person that she was naturally, that was all that was required.

I thought of her as soon as I opened my eyes in the morning and she was the last thing I thought of when I went to bed at night. If my mind wasn't actively engaged in some work or task, the 'default' setting was her. I thought of her constantly, where she may be, what she might be doing, when would I see her next? If I closed my eyes I could see every part of her dear, sweet face, a face that I knew wasn't perfect but through my eyes, eyes filled with my love for her, she was the living embodiment of all the great and fabled beauties of history, from Helen of Troy forward throughout time, to the present day, all wrapped up in one.

Yes, I could see her nose wasn't perfectly straight, yes, her teeth, good as they were and white as they were when she smiled, weren't toothpaste advert perfect and her top lip, kissable as it may have been, was just a little on the thin side. But to me there has never been another living soul who can make my heart beat so fast, or who can melt me heart with a smile like she can. I could look at her face for hours, and never tire of it and I couldn't imagine life without her. She became my ideal woman, and has remained my ideal woman through everything life has thrown at us.

Suffice to say that we eventually moved in together and a few years down the line we married. We've had a good life together and of course we've had our ups and down as every married couple do but throughout it all, one thing has remained constant, our love for each other. She can still take my breath away with her smile and when I come home, and maybe surprise her engrossed in some task, she turns and looks at me as if seeing me for the first time. That look of love and the smile she gives me when she turns and sees me there, lifts my heart beyond anything you could imagine.

I know if I live to be a hundred, I'll love her until the day I die and, when we're both old and gray, my love for her will be undiminished and as strong as it has ever been. She is, and will remain, as beautiful to my eyes as that first day I met her at the university, so many years before. Some things are worth getting out of bed for.

22. THE EMBRACE

This story was told to me by an old family friend of my father, and is set many years ago in the early 1950's. He was a down to earth sort of man, quiet and unassuming, very practical in his outlook as befits a man of science, an engineer, although he was already retired by the time he told me this story a few years ago. He wasn't given to flights of fancy or airy fairy ideas about the supernatural and the story he gave me was told in a very matter of fact way. I was left in no doubt that he was telling the truth, and he didn't care whether I believed him or not, for to him, these were the simple facts.

'I was visiting Aberdeen, and had been invited to stay with an old University friend,' he began. 'We'd been out for an evening meal, and had a pint of beer in the local pub before we came home. Believe me when I say, we were in no way drunk, or even approaching an inebriated state by the time we got home. And when I say a pint, that's all it was, one single pint of beer. His parents were still up and about, for in those days the pubs closed at 10pm, and we were back well before closing time. They stayed in a large house on Queens Road, which was and still is, one of the most prestigious areas of Aberdeen. We chatted for some time, and his parents proved to be good company, his mother providing us with tea and biscuits as we played a few hands of cards. All in all, it was a very enjoyable evening.

In those days people had much simpler pleasures and lifestyles, listening to the radio, playing board games, cards etc. At that time, in the early 1950's, television was an unusual and rare thing and there was very little noise in most houses apart from the sound of the day to day living of the household - and the radio when it was turned on.

It was winter time. The weather had deteriorated since we had returned 'home' and the wind howling around the house sounded rather spooky, prompting me to say it was an excellent background sound for the telling of ghost stories. I meant it in a light hearted manner, a simple throwaway remark but I could tell by their reaction that something wasn't quite right. His parents exchanged furtive looks and my friend looked at the floor as if embarrassed.

'Please don't make fun of ghosts in this house,' his mother said. 'We have been reliably informed that one of our guest rooms is haunted, although none of us have ever had the nerve to sleep in that particular room, to confirm or deny the story.'

Surprised by the very idea of a haunted room I rose to the challenge at once.

'A haunted room? That sounds like a challenge to me,' I exclaimed, 'please let me stay in it. I don't believe in ghosts, and I'd rather like to put it to the test.'

Again his parents looked at each other as if thinking it

over, his father shook his head almost imperceptibly.

'We couldn't let you do that,' his father said. 'What if you came to some harm, we'd be held responsible. Or if you were so frightened that you had a heart attack, or such like? We'd never forgive ourselves. No, I don't think it's a very good idea at all.'

He shook his head as if to reinforce what he'd just said, but undeterred I tried my level best to persuade him.

'I don't wish to go against your advice sir,' I began respectfully, 'but I'm a young, healthy and very fit person. I play rugby every Saturday, train three of four times a week, so let me assure you sir that the likelihood of me having a heart attack are virtually impossible. I'm a very practical chap, a man of science, an engineering graduate as you know, and not given to flights of fancy.'

All this was said with a smile on my face and not the slightest bit confrontational. I liked my friend and his parents too much to ever think of being disrespectful to them. Again he shook his head.

'Oh, I don't know,' he said, now sounding half persuaded, but shaking his head again, 'I have a bad feeling about this, I'm just not convinced that it would be a good idea at all.'

Sensing the doubt in his mind, I pressed my case.

'At the moment,' I said, trying to sound as reasonable as possible, 'we don't even know if the room is haunted, do we? It's only a third party report, a rumour. There's probably nothing wrong with the room at all, just some fanciful story from god knows who, a servant, a maid or such like, from many years ago. Have any of you ever heard or seen anything in the room?'

I looked at his parents, still smiling as I said it.

'No,' his mother replied. 'None of us have seen or heard anything. But that room is always cold, even in the height of summer. It doesn't,'... and she hesitated, searching for the right words, eventually settling for, 'feel right... it just doesn't feel right to me,' she concluded.

'Well, isn't this a great chance for you to find out for certain, to dispel the rumours,' I wheedled. 'It seems a shame to me for a perfectly good room to go to waste on the strength of an unconfirmed, and most likely untrue, story.'

His father sighed in resignation. His mother moved closer to his father, taking his arm as if huddling together for comfort.

'Very well, but on your own head be it,' his father said, finally relenting with a note of resignation in his voice. 'I hope it's understood that I take no responsibility for anything that may happen in that room. In fact, I want that in writing before I allow it,' his father said firmly.

He was a solicitor, and cautious by the very nature of his profession. I readily agreed to sign anything exonerating them from all fault.

Now that they had reluctantly agreed, his mother at once took charge and suggested that my friend and I had better prepare the room for my stay. A fire should be lit, the room opened up to 'air' it and the bed made up. Within minutes we had all gone upstairs to the room in question, which lay at the end of a short corridor.

His mother selected a key from the large bunch of keys she had taken with her and unlocked the door but stepped aside to allow my friend and myself to enter the room first. It smelled musty from disuse, the light-switch just inside the doorway to my right responded with a weak, dim glow, which seemed to add more gloom to the room than light. His mother went over and bent down beside the brass bedstead to switch on the bedside lamps. Now the room looked more inviting, the light warmer, although the room itself was distinctly chilly.

'Look at the dust in here,' his mother said apologetically, and then looking at me she asked. 'Well, what do you think?'

I smiled at her.

'It looks a perfectly comfortable room, and I'm sure with the bed made up and a nice roaring fire to take the chill off the air, I shall spend a very restful and peaceful night here' I declared confidently.

I have to say, she looked somewhat doubtful.

The next half hour or so was taken up with more

practical aspect of my stay in the room. My friend and I managed to get a fire going in the hearth. We brought up kindling and coal in a big brass coal scuttle but first, scrunching up some old newspapers, we set them alight to get the kindling started. Once the kindling wood started to burn we carefully placed some smaller pieces of coal round and over it. Eventually we could see the fire was well alight and loaded some larger pieces of coal on too. It was a fire which should keep the room warm for a good number of hours. It would be much needed, for in those days before universal central heating, it would be the sole source of heating on this cold Aberdeen winter night. Ghost or no ghost.

While we had been attending to the fire, his mother had brought some dusters and dusted all the furniture, 'tut-tutting,' to herself, all the while. The bed was then made up, and now with the fire rapidly taking the chill from the air and the bedside lamps casting their warm glow over everything, the room looked very inviting.

Now that the room was made habitable again, we all went downstairs and his mother, ever the perfect hostess, made us some cocoa before bed. We talked for a little bit longer but with the time now well after 11pm we eventually made our mutual ways upstairs.

The bathroom was just along the landing from my bedroom and so after brushing my teeth, I made ready for bed. I undressed, hanging my clothes carefully over the back of a chair so as not to crease them. This was back in the days before man-made fibres and non crease materials and we were a bit more careful of how we looked after our clothing back then. Putting on my pyjamas, I turned back the sheets and blankets. But before getting into bed, I added a few more lumps of coal to the fire which was already throwing a pleasant heat into the room.

I had a quick look round the room and even looked into the substantial wardrobe, 'just in case,' I thought. Just in case of what I asked myself with some amusement, but I admit I looked all the same, under the bed too and then I switched off the bedside lamp at the far side of the bed before getting into bed and getting myself settled.

'Well, here goes,' I said to myself and switched off the remaining lamp at my side of the bed.

The light from the fire cast a warm, friendly, but dim light over the room, the shadows restless with the movement of the flames. I lay awake for some time wondering if something would happen and what it might be. But eventually, the combination of heat and tiredness meant I must have fallen asleep.

I awoke slowly, slowly, disorientated, from my sleep, my thought processes slow to 'come round' and understand. The fire in the grate had died a little but it was still burning and still possible to make out my surroundings from its light.

The old, heavy furniture, the pictures on the wall, the ornaments on the mantelshelf. Despite that, I felt cold, so incredibly cold that I was shivering. I remember thinking, 'I shouldn't be as cold as this, the fire is still burning the room should be warm.'

I thought for another moment or two, trying to puzzle this out, and with a growing awareness, I realised with a start that the cold was coming from behind me. I half turned, and stretching out my hand felt the sheets at the other side of the bed – they were freezing, so cold my hand felt as if it had been burned. I snatched my hand away, and turned back, thinking perhaps I should turn on the bedside lamp to investigate further. It was so cold I was reluctant to get out of bed, for all my instinctive reasoning told me that it must be colder in the room than under the sheets and blankets, so I lay there for a moment, working things out in my head. Call me dull-witted, or slow if you like but I still hadn't connected what was happening with any possible, 'haunting,' of the room.

I soon became aware that the cold at the other side of the bed now seemed to have moved over, closer to my side of the bed. I felt as if someone, or something was behind me. Then, a definite nudge against my back, someone *was* in bed with me, I thought, and then, as I panicked and tried to propel myself out of bed, I distinctly felt two freezing arms encircle me and pull me back into the middle of the bed, back

203

into a bone chilling embrace. Now, I wasn't just panicked, I was terrified. I've never felt so scared in my entire life, neither before nor since. Despite my fear and panic, I distinctly remember thinking, 'Whatever you do, don't mess the bed.'

Even in the throes of the freezing embrace I was sweating profusely with fear, the cold and the panic making me gasp for breath too. But worse was to come and I thought I felt cold lips kiss my neck. Then a smell so foul I almost vomited. I've never been a religious man but at that moment I called on god and all his angels to help me. The cold embrace seemed to be growing tighter by the second and I struggled even more violently, but to no avail, I was held fast, and I knew, I just knew, if I was to survive the night with my sanity preserved, I had to break free of my ghostly lover's embrace.

I've always been physically strong and in sheer desperation, I managed to throw my legs forward out from under the bedclothes and out of the bed, half lifting myself and getting my feet on the floor. As soon as my feet hit the floor the embrace ceased, as suddenly as it had begun. I hastily made for the door where the light switch was and then turned on the main light, eventually daring to look back at the bed, but there was nothing there. The bedroom was empty apart from myself; the fire burned cheerfully, as if nothing had ever happened. I found the courage to switch on the bedside lamps too – they glowed warmly casting their pleasant homely light over everything. I was still shivering, although sweat was dripping from me, but it was from fear, not the cold. Indeed, the room once more felt pleasantly warm.

I dressed quickly, desperate to get out of the room. Taking a pillow and some covers from the bed, I crept downstairs and made myself as comfortable on the large sofa in the lounge as my recent unwelcome visitation would allow. I slept, through sheer exhaustion after my ordeal, but rather fitfully it has to be said, constantly awakening at the slightest sound. It was there my friend's father found me in the morning. He knew at once from finding me there that something had happened and invited me through to the large kitchen where he had already put on the kettle to make tea. He waited patiently, first placing a cup of hot tea before me, allowing me to gather my thoughts before saying just one word.

'Well?'

I looked at him, still trembling as I thought of the events of the night before.

'The room isn't right, sir, seal it off, lock the door, throw away the key, and never let anyone sleep there again,' I declared.

'Is it that bad?' he asked.

I nodded, sipping the hot, sweet tea.

'It's worse than bad, it's absolutely terrifying. Whatever it is, it's something really evil. I thought I was going to die in that room.'

I told him the entire story, and by the time I finished, he too was white faced and shaken.

'We mustn't tell my wife,' he said. 'I'll move everything out, and lock the door as you advised. I'll even write the story down and leave it in the room as a warning for future owners to be aware of.'

We agreed to tell his wife that I thought I had seen something in the middle of the night and had been badly frightened, but nothing specific and nothing more. Just enough to account for him locking off the room and staying out of it for the rest of their time there.

I told my friend of course, after all I thought, he may inherit the house one day and it would never do to leave him in ignorance of something as terrible as that haunted guest room. We stayed friends for many years and I occasionally visited him in Aberdeen, quite happy to stay overnight with the family but obviously never in that particular room again.

* * *

With the story now passed on to my care, curiosity got the better of me, and one day, when I was in the area, I decided to go and have a look at the house on Queen's Road, where the events of this story had taken place. Like so many of the grand old mansions and family homes on Queen's Road, I found that the building is now in the hands of an oil company and has been turned into offices. Perhaps the entity has been laid to rest – who knows, for it seems, for the foreseeable future that nobody will ever sleep in that room, or that house again.

23. THE WRANG HAND

This is a wee story I got from my brother, who had it tucked away in his memory but didn't realise it was of any value until we were talking of similar events recently with other members of our Stewart family. I had told a strange story months previously, about an event that took place in early 2017. And when they asked me to tell them the story again, which I will now recount to you before I tell the main story, it had triggered the memory of this tale in his head.

I had been in bed, in a really deep sleep, when I was woken in the early hours of the morning by our front door bell ringing. I sat bolt upright in bed, wide awake, absolutely convinced the door bell had rang. I had heard it and I knew it was our door bell, loud and clear. I was just about to get out of bed to see who was at the door but then I hesitated. I looked at the bedside clock. It was 4am exactly and, slightly confused, I tried to rationalise what I'd just heard. I knew I had heard the door bell, it was unmistakeable, but what really stopped me getting out of bed was the plain simple fact that we don't have a door bell! At least not a functioning one, for the simple truth is that there is a door bell in place, but it hasn't worked for around 25 years. When the exterior of our original wooden front door had been painted many years ago, the painter had unscrewed the box with the doorbell button, and somehow or other it had been lost and never replaced. Now there are simply two bare wires sticking out of the small drilled hole where the button used to be and there is no earthly way it could be rung.

The next day, I quite light heartedly told the story on the internet, knowing it would interest and maybe spook some of my traveller relatives. I knew what they would think; it was a death warning, for amongst travelling people, there is a belief or superstition that when the death of a relative is approaching, members of the family may receive a 'warning' or a heralding of the death. Sometimes unexplained lights appear or 'death candles' as they are known, while others hear a loud knock or ring at the door or window.

Sure enough, as expected, I had a number of replies to my posting on social media from various cousins and relatives, all intrigued by my story and all predicting that I would soon hear of the demise of a relative. However, there is another chapter to the tale, for my brother Willie, dropped in past my house the very same day and asked me to tell him what had happened. So I told him the story and he sat there and listened without interrupting. He smiled when I finished, then told me his story.

He lives in Peterhead, about 30 miles from where I live. Like me, he had been in bed fast asleep when he had been wakened by someone outside his bedroom window singing. At first he thought it was just some drunken party goers passing by his house, as his bedroom is at the front of the property. So he decided to ignore it and try to get back to sleep but the singing persisted and it became all to obvious that whoever was singing wasn't just passing by the house, they were directly outside his bedroom window.

'I got oot o' bed tae see fit bam wis causin' a disturbance. I wisnae in too good a mood at bein waukened by some drunk. I pulled back the curtain tae see fa it wis, and the singing stopped deid, like somebody switchin' aff a light. I looked and looked but I could see nithing, so I went back tae bed. I remember looking at the clock,' he continued, 'it was four o'clock in the mornin.'

Amazing coincidence, or was there some other explanation for it? Don't ask me, I have no answers. I will just add that a close cousin did indeed die a short time later, but then again that may just have been a coincidence and you are free to draw your own conclusions.

Now that I have regaled you with these two interconnected stories I'll pass on to the main tale to be told.

My grandfather, auld Davy Stewart, known to some as 'Shooting Hill Davy,' passed away on November the fifth, 1972 at the grand old age of ninety one. He had lived for many years on the Shooting Hill, or Shooting Greens, as it was sometimes called, situated between Strachan and Potarch on the Deeside, hence his, 'by-name,' of 'Shooting Hill Davy.'

Travellers often use nick-names, or 'by-names' to differentiate between one family member and others with the same name. Older travellers frequently had large families, but used a limited range of names and since it was customary for travellers to name their children after members of their close family, it often led to further confusion. For instance, I have a number of cousins called, Davy Stewart, all named after our grandfather and a few cousins called Margaret, all named after my own mother.

Prior to auld Davy passing away he had been ill, bed bound and deteriorating for a number of months. He needed constant care and the family had taken it upon themselves, to make sure there was always a family member there, night and day. They worked out a rota system and certain sons and daughters took their turns at looking after him, doing the best they could for the old man. My brother was told this story by one of my uncles.

'It was getting late kind one night and I was jist aboot tae lie doon tae sleep, but I heard a sound, like somebody speaking in my father's room. Thinking he maybe needed a drink o watter, or a cup o tea or something, I went through, and spoke tae him. He was up on one elbow, looking across the room, and I askit him fit he was wantin.'

'Nithing, I wis jist speakin tae my mither,' he replied.

Puzzled my uncle spoke again.

'There's naebody here, da,' he said. But the auld man

was adamant.

'Aye, she's here, look, there she is,' he said, looking at a fixed point in the room and nae looking at my uncle, 'She's comin tae me,' and he held out his hand to his 'mother.'

Thinking to comfort his father, my uncle reached out to take his father's hand in his, with the idea that perhaps the old man would think he was holding his mother's hand.

'So, I steppit forward and took his hand in mine. Well, there wis an almighty "crack" and a thing like an electric shock ran up my airm and I was thrown half wye across the room. My da had slumped back on tae the pilla's. There was a queer smell in the room, like a fuse, or something electrical had blawn oot. I wis a bittie shaken like but I looked tae my father and he was breathing okay and seemed tae be sleeping peacefully. I left the room but I thocht aboot it and thocht aboot it, and I hardly had a wink o' sleep that nicht, but in the hinder end, I jist kent that his mither had come tae "tak him" and I had accidentally gotten in atween them. It wis an affa queer experience onnywye, yin that I've thocht o' a lot, but I'll never ken for sure fit it was. God rest his soul, but my da passed awa a few days later. It wis jist his time and his mither came for him, I'm sure o' it,' he concluded.

A few years later my brother was speaking to a woman who professed to be a medium and told her the story. She was thrilled to hear it and offered the explanation that when a spirit manifests itself on this plane, it needs to draw a

212

great deal of, 'energy,' to itself. What had happened to my uncle, she explained, was that just as my grandfather and the spirit of his mother were about to 'connect' my uncle had interposed his hand in the way and the energy had been discharged through him, causing the 'electric shock' phenomenon and the 'ionisation' or ozone smell in the room which followed.

Was that a reasonable, or just a fanciful explanation? Again, make up your own mind. I can only say that the uncle involved was not one for believing in ghosts or such things, or given to imaginings, so we have no reason to doubt what he said.

24. MY DEAR AUL FRIEN

This story is, once again, based on one of my songs. I deliberately left the song ambiguous as regards their relationship – it could be about sisters, brothers, cousins, or even a husband and wife. For the purposes of this story only, and because I am male, I will write it from a male standpoint. You may wish to take your own view, but the, 'twa aul friens,' have been together since they were children. Their story is a universal one from the travelling people, almost a racial memory, and every old traveller would have told you the same story if you had the chance to speak to them. They told how they were treated as outsiders when they went to school, bullied, name called and taunted by the settled children, how they got the blame for any mischief, or anything bad that happened. Little wonder then that they were delighted to go back on the road to live a freer lifestyle when springtime came, but a lifestyle that was hard too. No matter where they set up camp, they were soon moved on, unless it was working for a farmer to help with the crops and even then they were moved on when their usefulness was at an end.

* * *

My hert was brakin as I lookit doon upon ye, sae caul' and sae pale. The tears blinned my een as I thocht o' the years we had been thegither. I couldna mind on a time fin ye were nae there by my side,

214

sharin a' my joys, my happiness, and my pain and hurt as weel.

Growing up thegither, we lookit oot for each other ayewis, you watched my back and I watched yours, I covered up for you and you for me, and mony a hiding ye saved me fae, and me you.

Noo, as I gaze doon upon yer face for the last time, grief stricken, the years roll awa and memories flood in upon me. I remember oor first day at school, dressed in oor new school claes, washed and combed, schoolbags on oor backs gan through the school gates wi oor mithers, god rest their souls. Aye, it didna tak lang for the aulder bairns, the country ruchies tae start cryin us tinkies and worse, the younger yins seen learned fae the aulder yins. And it was me and you and oor brithers, sisters and cousins against the hale school.

Nane o' us winted tae gyang tae the school, fit good wis it, we thocht? We kent the names o' a' the birds and animals, we kent the names o' ivery tree, bush and plant already and whit it wis used for. We could feed and groom the horses, tinker aboot wi an auld car or bike until it was workin', mak things oot o' the maist basic stuff, like claes pegs, or artificial floo'ers wi jist some crepe paper, a bit o' wire and a knife. We could snare rabbits, or net them using the dogs, or lie still by the banks o' a bonny burn and guddle troot.

We learnt by watching oor mithers and faithers,

215

watchin' as they bocht and selt things wi the country hantle, and toon scaldies. How tae strike a bargain, so that we could buy a thing at a good price and sell it on tae anither body at a profit. Life wis oor school, but that wisnae good enough for, 'the authorities.'

I think back tae that as I look doon on yer face, lined wi age noo, mindin how young and fresh we were gan tae the school, but jist tae keep the authorites happy, them wha laid doon the law. We had tae gyang tae the school tae get the twa hundred, 'attendances.' Being at the school for a hundred days, what a waste o' time that wis. Lucky for us the 'attendance,' was marked twice a day; first thing in the mornin' and again efter denner-time, itherwise we'd hae tae be at school for twa hundred days! I think we wid hae run awa if that wis the case. Once that wis done we could leave, an I mind we could hardly wait tae get back on the road and heid oot whaurever the notion teen us, or rather whaur the notion teen oor femilies. But it was at school that we learned oor ABC's and sums. We could a' coont weel eneugh onnywye, but the readin' wis a different metter.

I aye mind that first day we went tae the school, I could hardly understand a word the teacher said. She wis a richt bonny woman, bit she spoke gey queer like, affa posh, bit the teacher and the ither bairns thocht it wis US that spoke queer. Lookin back, I can see fit wye, for we spoke a mixture o' Scots and the cant. Scots wis bad eneugh, as far as the teachers were concerned, for they winted abody tae speak 'proper English' and mony a skelp on the fingers we got wi the teacher's ruler for sayin, 'aye,' instead o, 'yes.' The cant wis anither thing athegither and we soon learned nae tae use it and never tell the scaldie kinchens fit the words meant. It wis oors, and we were telt nae to tell whit it wis, or, 'ful the scaldies muns,' by oor mithers and faithers.

Aye, every day at school seemed like a battle. We were forever ha'in tae fecht and nae jist one tae one, sometimes at, 'playtime,' or coming hame fae the school, we were set upon by groups o' ruchie kinchens and had tae fecht oor wye oot o' it. Maist times we gave as good as we got but fae time tae time we got a leatherin. At times like that, I would mark oot fa wis the ringleaders and sooner or later I'd get them on their ain, fin there wis naebody else aboot and gie them a tannin in return. They wernae sae brave on their ane, like maist bullies.

It was a great relief tae us fin the spring came roon and we had oor attendance counted up, for syne we could tak oor leave o' the hated school and nae regrets. We couldna wait tae get back on the road and awa fae the school and the unhappiness that came wi it. So, once oor faithers started lookin oot the camps (tents) and the ither things we needed for traivellin', we kent it widnae be lang afore we bid fareweel tae the hoose we wintered in. I say, 'hoose,' bit we ken, noo that we're aulder, that it was little mair than a widden shack, wi a well about a hundred yards fae the hoose, wi anither widen oot-hoose, oot at the back, what they cried a, 'dry lavvie,' something that was very common in the country lang ago. It needed tae be emptied oot every so often, but my faither wid never allow onny o' us bairns tae dee that job. He wid hiv been too feart for onny o' his bairns takin ill.

Fin we set oot on the road, we aye traivelled in a group. Twa or three femilies thegither, including oor uncle Wullie and his femily, and oor auntie Lizzie and hers, so we niver lacked for company. Sometimes there wid be ither close relatives, or we'd meet up wi ithers o' the femily at camp sites alang the road. It wis aye great tae see cousins, uncles and aunties we hidna seen since the year afore, as weel as ither femilies o' traiveller's, maybe nae so closely connected, but friens and acquaintances, weel kent faces and folk.

It wis funny how we we aye traivelled north first, working, buyin and sellin, whatever wid turn a profit, collecting copper and brass, fae the tradesmen in the wee toons. The women would visit the sma' ferms up the side roads wi their baskets, pegs and various items o' haberdashery, ribbons for the lassies, a pirn o' threid or twa for the hoose keepers tae sew and mend; combs, hair grips and sic like, for in those days lang ago, there wis nae supermarkets like there is noo-a-days and folk rarely wint tae the big toons. Finally, if nithing else, they would tell a fortune or twa in exchange for eggs, butter, cheese or whatever they could get. And sometimes they wid get money tae.

Sometimes a fermer wid offer some work, if he needed a hand tae get crops planted, or wis ower hashed wi ae thing or anither and we wid step in for a wee whiley. But we aye liked tae be on the move again as fest as we could. Headin tae the next camp site, exchanging information, fa wis a good, 'mark,' (client) fit fermer was shan gadgie, a pure guffy, or fa wis a barry gadgie tae work for.

In this wye we worked oor wye roon the country, meeting relatives and friens alang the wye and aye makin a living. Sometimes we were up and sometimes doon but we were rarely stuck. If we were hungry then it was a simple metter, o' catching a rabbit for the pot, or guddling troot. Every fish wis a 'troot' tae us bairns and rabbits were plentiful as the countryside fair teemed wi rabbits.

Sometimes we wid set up a net, a lang net, twenty or thirty feet or so lang at one end o' a field and get doon tae the ither end wi the dogs. We set the dogs loose, driving the rabbits up the field and intae the nets where they were quickly despatched. The women would skin and "dress" the rabbits for the pot and the skins would be saved, for the rabbit skins could be selt and brought in a sma' income. Everything had value tae us and nithing was wasted.

D'ye mind gan tae the pearl fishin, the best river for it was aye the Tay, but there's nae fishin left noo and the pearl fishing has been banned. The scaldies came, lookin for easy money, oot fae the toons wi nae idea o' fit they were deein and destroyed thoosands o' mussels for nithing. In oor young days though, ye could still mak a wee bit aff the pearl fishing so it wis aye worth gien it try for a wee while, before heidin doon tae Blairgowrie for the berries.

The berries, noo that wis oor great traiveller meeting o' the year. Traivellers fae a' ower Scotland wid travel tae Blair to pull the berries, rasps mainly, and mak a few pounds before the winter set in. Us bairns wid work ana and mak enough tae buy oor shoes and claes for gan back tae school. It was a great opportunity to meet ither traiveller femilies, folk ye maybe hidna seen since the berries the year afore. Friens were made, aye and enemies as weel.

Roon the campfires at nicht sangs wid be sung, tunes played on the fiddle, accordion, or pipes. The young folk wid dance in the licht fae the fire and mony a couple met at the berries. A lassie micht come tae the berries wi one femily, and leave wi anither, sometimes wi the blessin' o' her femily, and sometimes an elopement wid tak place if the femily didna approve.

It wisnae a' happiness and good fun of course, sometimes aul rivalries and the enemies mentioned afore wid raise their ugly heids and then the 'blid and snotters' wid flee. Real men were expected tae hae a 'square go.' Nae kickin, nor stampin, nor weapons. Alcohol wis aften the cause o' the battles that took place and sometimes hale femilies wid get involved and it became a feud. Luckily this wis gey few and far atween.

Aye, and that wis how we passed oor youth and growin' years in the enclosed circle o' the traiveller femilies, only speakin and mixing wi the country hantle and toon scaldies tae mak a livin', or gyang tae school. They were aye suspicious o' us and we were suspicious o' them. I remember my auld granda warnin us.

'Niver trust the scaldie, for he'll be nice as ninepence tae yer face and cry ye a dirty tink ahin yer back. He'll steal onny thing he can and tell fowk it wis you whit done it eence ye've moved on and canna deny it.'

So we learned a mistrust o' the settled fowk, it wis weel dinned intae us. They lookit doon on us, cried us names, thieves, crooks, scum, dirty vermin and sic like, bit it wid have surprised them tae ken that we lookit doon on them jist as much. We lookit on them wi utter contempt, for as far as we were concerned, they were well-nigh useless. They workit for a 'bare wage' and were niver onny better aff, at the mercy o' their bosses wha could sack them at onny time if the notion took them, leaving them destitute, for withoot their work they didna ken fit tae dee. We on the other hand could dee jist aboot onny thing we wanted tae, turn oor hands tae onnything, mak a living using oor wits, buying and selling. It was a metter o' pride that we were to a' intents and purposes

221

self-sufficient.

The memories o' oor youth fill my mind as I tak yer ice-caul hand in mine, this hard working hand I hae teen in frienship at yer weddin, that had cradled my first born bairn in yer airms, as prood o, my bairns as ye were o' yer ain. The hand that wis aye there fin a help wis needed, that had offered money in hard times and comfort in harder times. Oh, whit a loss ye are gan tae be tae me.

Ye ken I wis niver a religious body, I didna hae the belief that you did. I niver believed in heaven and I believed even less in hell but, be that as it may, we niver tried to persuade each ither that oor opinion wis the richt yin, the yin that mettered. You had your belief and I had mine. It was never a great thing atween us and noo here we are at the partin o the wyes. I'll niver see yer dear face again efter this day, unless of course, you were richt and I wis wrang.

Whaur iver ye micht gyang noo, yer weel prepared, for the life o the traiveller has been a lot like this fin I think on it. If there is an efterlife, weel I canna tell, but a' oor lives we seldom kent whaur we were ga'in fae one day tae the next. We wid get up in the mornin, and maybe be moved on by the hornies, (police) or the fermers, landowners, the council gadgies and sic like. Sometimes, we wid hae a plan, whaur tae gyang next but maist times we wid just set oot and see whaur the road wid tak us. It seems tae me, that this final journey is a bit like that. Yer maybe jist settin' oot upon a road again, a stranger road than we've ever been, but this last bit o' road ye mun tak yersel and I canna come wi ye, canna help ye. And so I wish for your sake that yer belief is true and there is something better waitin' for ye beyond this life.

Maybe if ye were richt, we micht meet up again. And if yer god dis exist. And if by some chance ye are welcome in this heaven, or paradise, and I canna see fit wye ye widna be, for ye niver did onny body onny herm in a' the years I kent ye, maybe there will be a wee corner o' this heaven o' yours set aside for traivellers. Whaur we could traivel aboot fae place tae place and pitch oor camp, or caravan and nae be shifted on until ye winted tae shift wirsel. A place whaur it's aye sunny and it's summer the hale year lang. A place whaur ye can sit at the end o' the day, yer belly ful, a dram in yer hand, a rare campfire burnin', wi good company and lovin friens aroon us. Aye, that would be paradise richt eneugh, and wid dee jist grand for us, and oor friens'.

25. ASHYPELT

This is a traditional story which I have been reliably informed by one of my cousins, was told to my grandmother, and her brothers and sisters, in the 1880's, by my great grandmother, Margaret Hutchison, who was married to Scottish piping champion, 'Crichie,' Donald Stewart. I remember my mother telling me this story when I was a young boy, probably from the age of four or five up until I was perhaps, eight or nine. She would tell it once or twice a year, but no matter how much of it I had forgotten after so many years, I always remember the witches chant, which you will learn too as the story progresses.

Much of the tale had faded from my memory, apart from the salient parts, but it's often the small details that help build the story and add flavour. Luckily, she often looked after my son, Robert, as a small child, before he went to school. And then again, he would sometimes stay with her overnight at the weekend, or during the school holidays, and she would tell him the story too. Between us we've managed to bring it back together again. I am also aware that some families may well have variants of the same story, but that's to be expected. It's what's known as the 'folk process' and it just means that when things are passed down orally, they get slightly changed each time.

* * *

Many, many years ago, there lived a widow woman who had three daughters. They lived in a grand old house on the outskirts of town. But despite its outward grandeur, the interior of the house was virtually empty, for the family had fallen on hard times. With the death of her husband who had been lost at sea the previous year, the ship, its cargo, and their family fortune had followed him into the watery depths. She had sold off nearly every piece of furniture, the fine paintings, the family silver, the family tapestries and linen, even her best dresses and jewellery, until at last they were virtually destitute. Where once there had been dinner parties, balls, enjoyment and gaiety, now all was bleak and cheerless. No servants now at her beck and call. With three young daughters to feed she was at her wits end, so she called the eldest daughter, Constance, to her.

'We have nothing left to sell my dear Constance,' she explained, 'and within a month or twa we will be facing starvation. You're auld enough noo to ken the truth, and take some responsibility for the family fortunes. You must go forth, oot intae the world to seek your fortune, get a job o' some sort, and help your younger sisters and me, otherwise we will all starve.'

Well, Constance, was none too pleased. She'd known nothing but luxury all her life, always well dressed in the finest of clothing, well fed and trained in many ladylike accomplishments, such as drawing, sewing, playing the harpsichord and the art of conversation, as many daughters of the gentry were in those days. She'd been thoroughly spoiled by her doting father but upon his death she, like the rest of the family had lost everything and now she would have to go out and work. The very thought offended her.

'Oh bother,' she snorted, stamping her foot in a wee tantrum. 'What kind o' job, and where would I even start tae look?' She scowled at her mother is if it was all her fault.

'I don't know,' her mother whined ineffectually. 'A job... just a job, it's what folk do, I hear. In the morning, take some of your clothes with you in a wee bundle and I'll bake you a rare, tasty bannock tae take with you, tae keep you going until ye find a job.' So the next morning her mother made ready to bake her daughter the bannock.

'Will ye take the wee bannock with a bless, or the big bannock with a curse?' her mother asked, hoping Constance would settle for the wee bannock with the blessing, since the big bannock would further deplete their dwindling food supplies. But undeterred, the eldest daughter replied that she'd have the big bannock with the curse, for she cared nothing for superstition and cared even less for how little was left for the rest of the family when she was no longer there. So the bannock was baked and, with her bundle over her shoulder, she set out to seek her fortune.

She walked and walked for many a mile, asking here

226

and there if anyone had a job they could give her, but always the reply came that times were hard and the poor folk had no jobs themselves and precious little to eat too. Eventually footsore and tired, she sat down on the roadside near a spring or well, thinking to eat a little bit of her bannock and have a drink of water to slake her thirst, for it was a hot day. She ate a mouthful of the bannock and was just about to take a drink of the crystal clear water she could see flowing from the spring, when a wee dog appeared.

She looked at it in disgust, for it was the scabbiest, mangiest, ugliest, dirty auld dog she had ever seen. The dog dragged itself up to her, for it was weak with hunger and to her surprise, it spoke.

'Oh bonny lassie, I am fair weak with hunger. I've had nothing tae eat for weeks upon end. I only ask for the crumbs that fall from your mouth, give me the crumbs that fall from your mouth.'

Well, the lassie looked at the dog, and took a swiper o' a kick at it.

'Get oot o' here,' she shouted, 'you'll get nothing from me, ye scabby wee mongrel. I'll nae waste a single crumb on a dying dog,' and she took another kick at him.

The dog scampered off into the bushes.

'Enjoy your drink from the spring lassie,' he said as he left, which reminded her how thirsty she was and she went to the spring to drink, but recoiled in horror, for the lovely crystal clear water she'd seen not five minutes ago was now red with blood and she could see things, unspeakable things, floating in it. Still thirsty, she had no other option but to travel on and she walked for many a long mile until eventually she could see the day was drawing to a close.

She came upon a cottage near a dark and lonely wood and knocked at the door. An old man came to the door, looking at her suspiciously.

'Aye lassie,' he asked. 'What can I dae for ye?'

'I've left home to seek my fortune and I've walked for miles and miles. I've found nae work and it's growing late and will soon be dark.'

The auld man nodded, that fact was self-evident for night was falling as they spoke.

'Could you give me lodging for the night, and I'll work for you in return, I'll work really hard, please?' she pleaded, hoping the auld man would say she could come in, for she didn't want to be left outside in the dark all night, but he slowly shook his auld gray head.

'Nah, lass, I've nae room, nor nae work for you neither,' he replied, rubbing his chin as if thinking.

He came out of his cottage and pointed upwards to a distant hill.

'D'ye see yon licht upon yonder hill. Ye'll get lodgings there,' he said, and having pointed the way, he bid her good fortune and returned to his cottage closing the door quietly behind him.

The lassie set out at once heading for the hill, keeping her eye on the light so as not to get lost. Little by little it drew nearer. It was well after dark by the time she reached the cottage, which sat in a clearing on the edge of another wood. Even by the light of the moon she could tell it was run down. The shutters of the windows were half hanging off, the light in the house shone out through cracks in the door. But beggars can't be choosers she thought, and it seemed infinitely preferable to sleeping outside in the woods, where a wild boar might gore her with its tusks, or a wolf eat her. So timidly, it has to be said, she knocked on the door and waited. She eventually heard a shuffling noise and finally the door creaked open on hinges which hadn't seen a spot of oil or grease in many a long year.

'What is it, wha is it that disturbs a poor auld woman at this late hour, and what dae ye want?' the old crone croaked.

Frightened, for the old crone looked like the evil witch in every book of fairy stories she had ever seen, the lassie asked if she could have lodgings for the night.

'Aye, I suppose you can, but ye'll hae tae work for it,' the witch said, for that's how Constance already thought of her.

'Can ye sew, can ye cook, clean and polish, and mind yer ain business, and nae go rakin' through an auld body's private belongings?' she rasped.

To every question, Constance assured her she was well qualified to perform her duties as required and so the old crone invited her in, and offered her some supper.

'It's only porridge, but it will fill yer belly,' she said gruffly ladling a generous portion into a wooden bowl.

The young lass, being hungry, ate it with relish, for to give the old woman her due the porridge was delicious and so the lass soon finished it.

'Weel, it's getting late and I've had a hard day, so I'm awa tae my bed,' the old crone announced, making for the stairs, which led up to some attic Constance speculated, for she had seen no second story to the cottage when she had approached it earlier.

'There, under the stairs, there's a bed there,' the old woman said. 'Bar the door afore ye go tae bed, and sleep well, for I hae plenty of work for ye the morn.'

And with that the witch disappeared up the stairs. The lassie looked at the door to be barred and wondered why bother. A two year old child could have knocked it down, it was so rotten and flimsy. But anxious to please, she did as she was told and made for bed. She slept well and arose refreshed in the morning, ready to commence her duties which were many and varied.

The cottage obviously hadn't been cleaned for some time but Constance set about her cleaning, determined to make a good impression on the old woman. She swept and cleaned, laid and lit the fire, fetched water from the well, set the water to boil in a big kettle, then washed the supper dishes from the night before, and the night before that, and the night before that too, by the look of it. She dusted and polished until the old woman came down the stairs and pronounced herself very happy with her efforts.

During the course of the morning the lass continued to work and tidy the vast stacks of books the old woman had lying on the table and every other surface. There were more books than she'd ever seen before but she didn't try to read them, for she could see they were very special books indeed. Some of the pictures were, well... very strange, monsters and angels and all manner of creatures, which convinced her that her new mistress was indeed a witch.

After lunchtime the old woman announced that she was going out, that she'd be gone for an hour or two. She gave the girl strict instructions not to go up the stairs, nor to go down to the cellar under the cottage, for there were thing there that it would be best if the girl didn't meet with, which was the way she put it. Lastly, she turned to a neuk beside the fireplace. There hung a large leather bag, long and greasy looking from frequent handling, the girl surmised.

'On no account touch that bag, for it will be the worse for you if you do, and you will live to regret it... or... you may not.' And having uttered this dire warning, the old witch, hobbled out through the door, and away, in the opposite direction from where the girl had come the night before.

Constance continued her duties but from time to time she cast a sideways glance at the long leather bag, wondering what might be in it, until at last she could contain herself no more and lifted the bag off the hook from which it was suspended. It was heavy, really heavy she thought and dragged it over to the table. It was a matter of minutes for her to untie the draw string and open the bag. She stood well back thinking there may be some kind of trap, or magic spell contained within but when nothing happened she went closer and looked inside.

The shine of the gold and silver coins almost took her breath away. The old witch was fabulously wealthy it seemed and for the first time Constance thought of her family starving back home. This bag and its contents could save them from starvation and so she resolved to take it at once, and be long gone before the old woman returned. And take it she did.

She hurried down the hillside path, the bag clutched to her bosom, looking fearfully behind her but saw nothing. Once she was on the level ground at the bottom of the hill she thought the witch would never catch her, for Constance was young and quick and the old witch was, well... old, and slow.

Passing a field, a scabby old cow, looked at her and

moaned with pain.

'Help me lass, help me, I haven't been milked for hundreds of years,' she said. 'Help me, help me, I haven't been milked for hundreds of years.'

And right enough, she was so grotesquely swollen with milk that she must have been in agony.

'Milk yourself, ye stupid auld coo,' Constance shouted as she passed. 'I'm in too much o' a hurry tae stop.' And she left the poor old cow, mooing with pain.

A good while later the old witch came hobbling along the same road, having come home and found her bag was missing. She saw the cow and asked it if she had seen her maid saying.

> *'Have ye seen a maid o' mine, goin' along this road,*
> *With a long wig-wag, and a long leather bag.*
> *And all my gold and silver?'*

'Oh aye,' said the cow. 'She passed by here a wee while ago, ye'll catch her if ye hurry.' So the old witch hobbled off as fast as she could go.

A little bit further on the lassie came to another field, and in this field there stood a really sorry excuse for a horse. It was so thin you could see every rib and bone in its body. Its backbone stood up like a razor blade and it was scabby and mangy, with tufts o' hair missing, big baldy patches all over It was knock-kneed as well. It was so weak, it could hardly lift its head up, and little wonder, for it seemed to have the biggest head she'd ever seen on a horse.

'Ride, ride me,' the horse whinnied, 'Ride me, please ride me, for I haven't been ridden for hundreds of years.'

Constance looked at the horse with undisguised contempt.

'Dinna be daft, ride ye? By the looks o' it ye can hardly stand, never mind trot or run. I can run faster than you myself, ye broken down old nag.' And with that she was away, hurrying homewards.

Very soon afterward, as the horse was eating a tasty tuft of grass, the witch hurried into view and asked the horse.

> *'Have ye seen a maid o' mine, goin' along this road,*
> *With a long wig-wag, and a long leather bag.*
> *And all my gold and silver?'*

'Aye, a bonny lassie, but very disagreeable,' the horse said. 'She's not long gone, keep going and ye'll catch her.'

The witch hurried on, desperate to recover her gold and silver.

A little further on Constance came to a high wall with an old rusty gate which she found hard to open. The rust on the gate seemed to have caused the hinges to seize up solidly. She was just about to attempt to climb over the gate when the gate spoke to her.

'Swing on me, please swing on me, for I haven't been swung on for hundreds of years,' pleaded the old gate, for it had enjoyed the children of previous generations swinging on it, in its youth.

'Nae me,' said the uncaring lass, 'I haven't the time, and you're just a useless, rusty auld gate that looks as if it will never open or close again,' and she made to climb over it.

The gate, insulted and angry, swung violently and Constance, not having a good hold, for she thought the gate would never move again, was tossed off into a thick patch of briars and thorn bushes. She struggled and struggled to free herself. But the more she struggled, the more she became ensnared, until at last what she feared came to pass and the old witch caught up with her.

The old woman cackled with glee and with one triumphant wave of her magic wand it was all over. The beautiful young woman was turned into a useless, white chuckie stone. The witch retrieved her long leather bag, with all her gold and silver, and went home.

* * *

After a week or so had gone by with no news, the mother called her second daughter, Isabella and told her the same things she had told Constance. Just like Constance she too was not very happy. She screamed and shouted and called her mother a useless old bag but the truth of course was that she was every bit as useless as her mother. However, faced with the same ultimatum, she too agreed to go out into the world to seek her fortune. Like Constance she also asked for the big bannock with the curse and so it was that she set out the next morning, with her bundle of possessions on her back and the big bannock with the curse wrapped in brown paper.

After walking for many miles, seeking employment here, there and everywhere without luck, she eventually came to the same overflowing spring by the roadside. Thinking it the ideal place to stop, for it was, she sat down upon the grassy verge to have a mouthful of her bannock and a drink from the crystal clear waters of the spring. She had no sooner broken off a piece of the bannock to eat, when the same scabby auld dog appeared, and much to her surprise spoke to her.

'I'm fair dying o' hunger, jist give me the crumbs that fall from your mouth, that's all I ask, the crumbs that fall from your mouth,' he repeated, pleading with her.

'What, a half deid scabby aul mongrel like you? The crumbs would be wasted, get oot o' here, away with ye,' she shouted and threw a stone at him, hitting him on the back leg.

He yelped, and dragged himself into the bushes. As she was chewing her mouthful of bannock, which in the heat of the day was dry going, she remembered the spring and she was about to go over to it for a drink of the fine cool water, when the wee dog looked out from the bushes.

'May ye enjoy your drink of water,' he growled at her, and she threw another stone at him, drawing another yelp of

236

pain.

As she bent down to drink some of the lovely cool water, she noticed that it was changing before her very eyes, and where there had been clear, cool water, there now ran thick, viscous blood, stinking and disgusting. She recoiled in horror and hurriedly left that place, thinking to get a drink elsewhere.

Just like her elder sister Constance, Isabella walked for the rest of the day, seeking work here and there but getting nothing, until at last she realised it would soon be dark. Anxious not to sleep outside in the woods, she quickened her pace, looking for some inhabited cottage or house, for although she knew little of the real dangers that lurked in the woods, she had heard tales of wolves eating girls like her and had heard so many stories of ghosts, bogles, and vampires, that she was altogether far too frightened to even contemplate the idea.

Following in her sister's footsteps it was almost inevitable that she would knock on the door of the same cottage on the edge of the same dark woods. The same old man opened the door and pointed to the same distant hillside, suggesting that she would get lodgings there, where she could see the light shining.

It had just turned dark when she came upon the ramshackle cottage with the broken shutters and warped door, which she approached with some trepidation, and knocked upon. The door almost burst open under the strain of her knocking, shivering in its frame, but held on bravely. Isabella heard a shuffling sound from within and then the door opened. The old woman asked the same question.

'Wha is it that disturbs a poor auld woman at this late hour, and what dae ye want?' she croaked.

'Please ma'am,' Isabella pleaded. 'I'm lost and frightened and I was wondering if ye could give me lodgings for the night, so I don't have tae sleep out in the wild woods and maybe get eaten by a wolf, or... or... a bear,' she finished.

'Come intae the light, so I can get a better look at ye,' said the old crone, whose eyesight wasn't very good if the truth be told. Isabella did as she was bid. The crone looked at her suspiciously. 'Ye look familiar,' she said, 'd'ye hae a sister by onny chance?' Isabella nodded.

'Yes, ma'am,' she answered, 'but she's at home with my mother, who has sent me out to seek my fortune and get a job. I've looked all day but found nothing, and now I'm exhausted, hungry, and frightened.'

'Weel, come on in then,' the crone invited her, 'I hae nithing tae eat, except a wee drappy porridge left ower fae suppertime, but ye can hae that. Mind you I expect ye tae work for it in the mornin' and if your onny good, then I can maybe gie ye a jobby as my maid.'

Isabella expressed her gratitude and was soon sitting

at the table with a large bowl of steaming hot porridge, which despite its humble nature, was absolutely delicious to the hungry young lass.

After Isabella finished the porridge she washed the dishes, to show how willing she was to work for her living. The crone expressed herself happy with her efforts and, as she shuffled off to bed, she told Isabella to make herself comfortable for the night on the bed under the stairs. Being tired and exhausted from walking all day, the warmth of the cosy cottage soon made her drowsy and she crawled into bed and slept like a log the whole night through.

She rose bright and early, refreshed from her slumbers and set about cleaning, sweeping, scrubbing. She lit the fire, put the big black kettle on to boil and any other tasks she could see that needed doing. Like her sister before her, she wondered at the nature of the many books scattered about the room. Curiosity getting the better of her she peeked inside but the words were in some language she didn't understand and the occasional picture of strange creatures and strange beings frightened her a little. She, like her sister before her, came to the inevitable conclusion that her new mistress was a witch.

After breakfast, the witch, as Isabella now thought of her, declared herself satisfied with the way Isabella had performed her duties and offered her the job as her maid, which Isabella accepted, 'until something better comes along,' she secretly thought to herself.

After lunchtime, the witch informed Isabella that she was very tired as she hadn't slept very well the previous night, and was going to have a, 'wee snooze,' requesting Isabella to wake her in about three hours. That's really quite a *big* snooze, Isabella thought, but said nothing, as the crone once more shuffled towards the stairs to go up to bed. With one foot on the first step, she turned to Isabella, and pointed to a neuk beside the fireplace. A large leather bag hung there, long and greasy looking, almost black with age and soot from hanging beside the fireplace.

'On no account touch that bag, for it will be the worse for you if you do and you will live to regret it.'

Having uttered this dire warning, the old witch 'peched' and grunted as she hobbled up the stairs. Isabella sat quietly, thinking about home for minute or two but soon smiled to herself as she heard the thunderous snoring of the old woman wafting down the stairs.

Isabella looked around the room, looking for something to do that wouldn't disturb her mistress as she slept and her eyes almost inevitably alighted upon the dirty old leather bag. Conscious of the warning, she tried to ignore it. Isabella however was cursed with almost insatiable curiosity, like most woman, and being a young girl, almost always did what she was told not to do.

Given the combination of these two factors, it was only

a matter of time before she sneaked over to the neuk and lifted the bag off the hook that it was suspended from. It was seriously heavy, she thought but she managed to lay it gently upon the table without making a noise. Untying the draw string, she peeked within. Her young heart raced with excitement, as a multitude of coins, gold and silver - but mostly gold - shone from the gloomy interior of the bag. Realising there was a fortune within the bag, which would keep her, her sisters and mother in luxury for the rest of their days, she determined to take the bag and its horde of gold and silver for herself.

She looked at the time, and realised that the old woman would sleep for hours yet. Gathering up her few possessions and with the bag clutched to her bosom, she was out of the door and away within seconds.

Isabella hurried down the hillside, anxious to get away before the witch woke up, for she was sure the old crone would do something truly horrible if she caught her. Fear of discovery hastened her steps but she reasoned that if she could get a good distance away then she would never be caught, for the old woman could hardly walk, never mind run, and she was... old, while Isabella was young and quick.

Bad fortune smiled upon Isabella that day, for the old woman suffered from indigestion which woke her early and she lay there for a minute or two, feeling very uncomfortable... and grumpy. Suddenly she realised the house was too quiet and rising from her bed quickly made her way as fast as she was able down the stairs. One glance was all it took for her to see, bad eyesight or not, that her treasure bag was gone and she hurried as fast as she could hobble in pursuit.

Almost at exactly the same moment that the witch discovered her bag had been stolen, Isabella was passing the field where the un-milked cow was standing and mooing plaintively.

'Milk me please, milk me, for I haven't been milked for hundreds of years,' the wretched old cow pleaded, and again, 'Please milk me, it hurts so much.'

Isabella spared the cow a quick glance and noted that she was really swollen but was so frightened that the witch would catch her, that she hurried past.

'Well, if you haven't been milked for hundreds of years, another year or two won't make any difference,' she said, cruelly dismissing the cow's pleas and rushed off as fast as she could manage.

A little while passed and then the witch came into view, hurrying to get her bag back if she could. Seeing the cow she asked her.

> *'Have ye seen a maid o' mine, goin' along this road,*
> *With a long wig-wag, and a long leather bag.*
> *And all my gold and silver?'*

'Aye, a cheeky wee besom, carrying a leather bag. She

242

passed here about five minutes ago,' declared the cow. 'She can't have gotten far.'

With that, the witch was off on the scent of her money.

Meanwhile, Isabella was approaching the paddock where the sorry excuse for a horse was grazing. The horse eyed up the pretty young girl and asked her politely.

'Ride upon me, ride upon me, for I haven't been ridden on for hundreds of years. Please, a quick gallop round the field, just once,' the horse asked nicely.

Isabella looked at the horse and laughed.

'A quick gallop, look at ye, you're so knock-kneed you'd likely trip over your own feet and if you managed tae break into a trot it would probably kill ye. I'd need a mountain of cushions, for your back bone is so sharp it would hurt tae sit on it.'

With those hurtful insults ringing in the ears of the old horse, she took off as fast as she could go.

Within a matter of minutes, the witch came to the field where the horse was looking over the dyke, and asked him.

'Have ye seen a maid o' mine, goin' along this road,
With a long wig-wag, and a long leather bag.
And all my gold and silver?'

'Aye, an impudent, disrespectful lassie, a richt cheeky wee midden. Scarce minutes ago, ye'll catch her at the gate if ye hurry,' he said.

Off the witch scurried but in a hobbling manner of

course.

By now Isabella was approaching the gate, which was closed. Try as she might, she could not get it to budge. It was rusted shut, she surmised but thought to herself, if she could get over that gate, the witch who was old and stiff would never be able to climb it and Isabella would never be caught.

'Swing upon me, please swing upon me, I haven't been swung on for hundreds of years,' the rusty old gate pleaded, desperately trying to recapture the glories of his youth, when he had enjoyed the attentions of the many children who passed his way.

'Deid no, nae me,' Isabella declared flatly. 'You're so rusted it would take me forever tae get you free, and I'll be caught.'

As she said it she put her left foot on the middle bar of the gate and swung her right leg over the gate, intending to jump off the other side. The gate, insulted by her callous attitude, summoned up all his strength and swung back violently, tossing Isabella into the same patch of briars and thorn bushes that Constance had fallen into. Try as she might, caught fast by the thorns snagging her clothes, she couldn't free herself. All her struggles just made things worse.

Within a few short minutes, Isabella's worst fears were realised when the old witch hobbled up to the briar patch. Seeing Isabella so helpless, scratched and torn, she laughed triumphantly and with one sweeping gesture of her magic wand turned the lovely Isabella into an ugly wee frog. She retrieved her bag of gold and silver once more and noted with even more satisfaction, and an ironic smile, that the ugly wee frog now sat upon a white chuckie stone; her sister.

* * *

With another week gone by, Ashypelt's mother sat with her head in her hands, lamenting the fact that neither of her darling girls had sent her a message to say they were gainfully employed and neither had they sent any money back to buy food. Now she only had one daughter left, and she, unlike her sisters had never considered hersel a grand lady, she liked nothing better than to mix with the common folk, especially the house servants, when they still had house servants before the hard times set in. She especially liked to help out in the kitchen and it was here she had earned the name of Ashypelt.

One day, while trying to help, she had accidentally tripped and fallen while carrying out a pail of ashes from the giant kitchen fires, to the midden. With the pail of ashes tipped over herself, she emerged pale and gray, like some small ghost. Everybody had laughed, for she looked quite comical and she had been dubbed, 'Ashypelt,' by her father, who loved her dearly. He knew she had a good heart, for he often saw her sitting quietly, or playing and skipping through the extensive gardens, feeding the small birds and

245

animals. The name stuck, and from henceforth, she was known affectionately by all as, Ashypelt.

'Mother, why don't you send me out to get work?' volunteered Ashypelt. 'I'll manage to get a job, I know I can.'

Her mother looked at her with doubt and not a little disdain.

'You Ashypelt, you? For god's sake lassie, dinna be daft. You're good for nothing else but tae rake aboot the fire in the kitchen, and mak a mess o' things. Ye haven't the wits ye were born with, how could you save us fae starvation,' she asked in rhetorical fashion.

'I'm as good as Constance, or Isabella,' Ashypelt said indignantly, 'better in fact.'

Her mother laughed and shook her head.

'I am, I swear I am,' said Ashypelt, 'just give me some job, some task to do, and I'll get it done, you'll see. I'll prove to you I'm no fool.'

'Very well, you silly lassie,' her mother said reluctantly. 'Take this auld pail and go doon tae the well, fill it with water and bring it hame. Can ye dae that?' her mother asked.

'Nae bother,' declared Ashypelt, thinking ye'd have to be a very special idiot if ye couldn't fill a pail of water and bring it home again. So she set out for the well. As soon as she dipped the pail in the well, Ashypelt knew she was in trouble, for there were small holes in the pail and the water quickly leaked out. She sat for a moment thinking how to fill the pail, puzzling over the problem, when suddenly one of the little birds she had fed in better days hopped up onto the edge of the well, and whistled cheerfully.

'Fill the holes with mud and moss, fill the holes with mud and moss.'

Taking the little bird's advice, Ashypelt filled all the holes with mud and moss. Now with the holes filled, the pail held the water. Thanking the little bird for her help, Ashypelt went home with a full pail of water for her mother. Her mother, who knew the pail was useless, was quite taken aback at the ingenuity of her supposedly dull-witted daughter.

'Well, I never,' she declared, 'I didn't think you had it in you Ashypelt, how very clever. You're obviously nae as daft as ye look,' she said, teasing her youngest daughter.

Ashypelt said nothing but just smiled secretively, thinking she wasn't as daft as her mother looked either.

Having tested her youngest daughter and been pleasantly surprised, and now at her wits end, the mother sat Ashypelt down and told her what the situation was.

'Well, there's nothing else for it mother,' she said, having now heard the full tale of woe. 'I'll have to go out into the big bad world, find a job and send some money home, otherwise we'll starve. I'm sure Constance and Isabella will find something too, and we'll do just fine, you wait and see.'

Her mother, having known far better times, wasn't so sure, but tried to encourage Ashypelt just the same.

'Okay now lass, here's what we'll do. You gather a few things about you, a change of clothes, your toothbrush and so on, and I'll bake you a fine bannock to keep you going for a day or two until ye get a job, how does that sound?' her mother said, trying to put a brave face on it.

Ashypelt was quite happy with her mother's suggestions and now the decision had been made was looking forward to leaving home and going off to seek her fortune, and adventure.

Next morning Ashypelt gathered her pitiful few belongings into a bundle and came downstairs. Her mother was in the kitchen, about to make the aforementioned bannock for the journey ahead.

'Now lass, would you like the big bannock with the curse, or the wee bannock with the bless?' her mother said, putting the same question to her that she had asked her other two daughters.

'Since it's so important that I succeed, I think the wee bannock with the bless would be best, don't you mother,' said Ashypelt, knowing there would be hardly any food left in the house for her mother once she had left, small bannock or not. The bannock, duly baked, was presented to Ashypelt by her tearful mother.

'Well, may god bless you my girl, may he help you find

a job, and bring you and your dear sisters home safely to me,' her mother intoned, and kissed Ashypelt's brow, and cheeks as a mother does.

Ashypelt took one last look round the house she had always called home and waving goodbye to her mother, set out on her journey.

Like her two sisters before her, Ashypelt walked for hours, seeking here and there, and thither and yon, but there was no work to be found until at last, hungry and thirsty she spied the well of fine spring water beside the road and stopped to have a mouthful of her bannock. Sitting under a shady tree, for it was close to noon and the sun was high in the sky, Ashypelt opened up her bundle and took out the bannock. Just as she broke a wee bit off, the same old, mangy dog appeared and looked at her with big, sad brown eyes.

'Oh, michty me bonny lassie,' he began, 'I'm dying of hunger, please give me the crumbs that fall from your mouth, that's all I ask, the crumbs that fall from your mouth.'

Ashypelt looked at the poor auld dog.

'Ye'll nae get crumbs from me auld dog,' she said, and breaking off another bit of the bannock, she shared it, with the poor pitiful creature.

Much to her surprise as the auld dog ate her precious bannock, it grew sleeker and fatter. The scabby mange disappeared and in its place a bonny wee doggy, happy and contented snuggled against her legs and licked her outstretched hand.

'Thank you lass, ye've been affa kind tae an auld dog. Ye have a good, and kind hert. May good fortune follow you all your days, but for now, have a drink before you continue on your way.'

Thinking this was good idea, and feeling rather thirsty since she had walked many miles in the sun, she bent down to slake her thirst. Much to her surprise, the crystal clear waters of the spring now ran red with the finest claret wine Ashypelt had ever tasted. Careful to only drink enough to quench her thirst, Ashypelt thanked the wee dog and taking her leave with one final pat of his noble head, set out once more in search of work and adventure.

She walked for many a mile and enquired everywhere for work but none was to be found, until at last she could see it was late in the day and it would soon be dark. Anxious to secure somewhere to stay for the night, she asked at every cottage and house she came across if she could have lodgings in exchange for some work but there was nothing. At last she came to the small cottage by the edge of the deep, dark woods. She knocked at the door and the old man duly opened the door. In response to her enquiry he came out of his cottage and pointed to the distant light that could now be seen as darkness slowly fell.

'Do you see yon licht on yonder hill,' he asked, and when she replied that she did indeed see 'yon licht on yonder hill,' he looked at her and said, 'weel, you'll get lodgings there.'

She thanked him for his kindness and leaving him standing at the door of his cottage hurried towards the light.

Ashypelt soon found that the light was further away than she had at first thought and it had been dark for some time by the time she walked into the clearing of the near derelict, run down cottage.

'Oh my,' she thought, unimpressed. 'It looks a bit of a hovel, still, beggars can't be choosers, and all that,' she told herself, and so, summoning all her courage she knocked on the flimsy door, which rattled in its warped frame.

'Wha's that? Wha wid disturb a poor auld woman, sae late at night?' came the cry from within, and after much shuffling of feet, the door creaked open, just a crack, and a bleary, bloodshot eye peered at her suspiciously.

'Please, ma'am, I'm just a young girl, alone and frightened, seeking lodgings for the night. If you would be so kind as to let me in and give me a place to sleep, even just on the floor, I would be very grateful and work hard to repay you,' she promised.

The door scraped open further and the old crone held a lamp up on high to see Ashypelt all the better.

'Have you been here before?' she asked, puzzled and slightly confused by the resemblance of Ashypelt to Constance and Isabella. Ashypelt shook her head vigorously.

'No, indeed not ma'am,' she replied, respectfully.

'I only left my home and my dear mother this morning to seek my fortune and to work for a living. I've never been here before. I think I would have remembered,' she added ironically.

Grudgingly, the old crone opened the door, and invited Ashypelt inside, barring the virtually useless door behind them.

Much later, her stomach nicely filled with the steaming hot porridge that was offered and accepted, she thanked her benefactor profusely and promised to work for her in the morning in return for her generosity. Quite soon the old woman announced that she was ready for bed and pointing under the stairs, told Ashypelt that she could have the bed there and wished her good night. Ashypelt, having had a most exhausting day, followed suit and in no time at all was fast asleep in the comfortable, cosy bed she found under the stairs.

The early morning sun shining in her eyes woke Ashypelt. Rising swiftly, much refreshed, she made ready the house for the old woman. She swept the floor, lit the fire, put on the big black kettle of water to boil and washed the supper dishes from the night before. She was careful not to disturb any of the books and papers strewn about on the tables and every available surface. Curious as all young women are, she had a little, 'nosey,' in them, but could make neither head not

252

tale of anything. None of the pictures, calculations, or diagrams made the slightest sense to her, although the pictures of demons, dragons and such like made her a little apprehensive. Her new acquaintance was a witch for sure, she concluded. But be that as it may, the old woman had taken her in, fed her, and given her a bed for the night and so Ashypelt felt obliged to work to pay off the debt.

Later that morning, after breakfast time, the old woman having noted how much work Ashypelt had done; the sweeping, washing and scrubbing, wood-chopping, hens fed, cow milked. She professed herself very pleased with Ashypelt and told her she could stay on as her maid if she wished.

After lunchtime the old witch, informed Ashypelt that she must visit a friend in a neighbouring village and would be gone for some time. She gave Ashypelt various jobs to be done before she left but took her leave with this warning.

'On no account go into the cellar under the house, for you may see things there that will not be to your liking,' she said. 'Likewise, do not go upstairs into my bedroom, there are things there you would not wish to meet.'

Ashypelt felt a shiver run up her spine as the old crone croaked out her warnings and was determined not to venture near the cellar or the old woman's bedroom.

'Finally,' she wheezed out her last warning, 'on no account open the long leather bag hanging in the neuk by the fireside.'

Ashypelt who hadn't even noticed the bag before, looked and saw it, hanging from a hook. It was almost black with age and accumulated soot from hanging by the fire and shiny with what looked like stains and grease. Having uttered all these warnings the witch hobbled out of the door. Away she went in the opposite direction from which Ashypelt had arrived the night before.

Having already done most of the main tasks before lunchtime, Ashypelt quickly finished doing what the old woman wanted her to do and began to 'potter,' finding little things to do, like dusting the many jars of god knows what she found on top of a cupboard. Remembering the words of warning, she stayed well away from the stairs and the door that led to the cellar. But her eyes returned again and again to the long leather bag. Finally, she could contain her curiosity no longer and, unhooking the heavy bag from its place beside the fireside, she took it over to the table near the window and untied the draw string. She was very careful, just in case there was something that she wouldn't want to meet or see in the bag. But all that met her delighted eyes was the shine of a great horde of gold and silver.

Taking a small handful of the gold and silver, Ashypelt quickly calculated that this one small handful of the treasure could keep her, her mother and sisters comfortably for a year at least. The whole bag would support them for the rest of their lives, or at least until her sisters found husbands for themselves. So, she returned the gold to the bag, collected her few possessions and, clutching the precious bag to her bosom, she left the cottage and set off down the hill as fast as her legs could take her.

In the meantime the grizzled old witch, having gone to visit her friend, found to her displeasure that her friend was not at home and so returned unexpectedly to find the door of the cottage wide to the wall and her new maid and her precious old leather bag gone. Absolutely furious, she set out at a fast hobble to recover her gold and silver, taking her best and most ferocious magic wand with her.

Ashypelt, like her sisters before her, was young and fast, and although she knew the old witch was... most probably, old and slow, she was taking no chances. She hurried on as fast as she could although the treasure bag was inordinately heavy.

As she was hurrying along, an old cow, looked over the dyke and mooed at her most pathetically, and said.

'Oh lassie will ye milk me? I haven't been milked for hundreds of years, and I'm in an affa lot o' pain. Please milk me.'

Ashypelt hesitated, she knew the witch may come home at any minute and find her gone but this poor old cow needed her help desperately. She couldn't find it in her heart to refuse, so she climbed over the dyke and set to milking the old, scabby cow. However as she milked, the old cow seemed to grow younger and younger, the scabby patches disappeared and her milk, at first thin and watery, grew rich and creamy. Ashypelt milked and milked until the cow could give no more.

'Thank you lass,' it said, 'you have such a kind heart, and we will meet again, but for now you must be on your way – hurry now, I will slow the old witch down.'

So Ashypelt took the cow's advice and hurried on her way, occasionally looking behind her to check.

A short time later the witch passed the very same field where the cow, now well milked and happy, stood chewing on some grass. Seeing the cow she chanted:

'Have ye seen a maid o' mine, goin' along this road,
With a long wig-wag, and a long leather bag.
And all my gold and silver?'

'Funny you should mention that,' the cow said, 'she was here just a few seconds ago, if you climb over the dyke, you'll probably find her hiding here behind the dyke.'

The old witch struggled to get over the dyke, for it was quite high and she was stiff and old, but eventually she managed it, driven on by her desire to get her treasure back. When she found herself in the field there was nobody there but her and the cow.

'Where is she?' screamed the witch, 'she's not here at all, you stupid cow, you're wasting my time, and now I have to climb back over this dyke again.'

'There's no need to climb over, here let me help you,' the cow assured her and charged the old crone who tried to run.

But even her fastest hobble was no match for the revitalised cow, who caught her on the end of its sharp, sweeping horns and threw her high in the air. Much higher than was strictly necessary to clear the high dyke, it has to be said. The witch flew through the air without need of a broomstick, and landed heavily in a crumpled heap on the other side once more. Dazed and confused, she lay there for some time, until, ever mindful of her gold and silver, she staggered to her feet and hobbled onwards cursing the cow.

Ashypelt, thanks to the cow, now had a sizeable lead over the witch but kept up a good speed nevertheless, until she eventually came to the paddock with the broken down old horse in it. When the horse saw her he staggered over to the dyke and whinnied to attract her attention.

'Ride me, please ride me, I haven't been ridden for hundreds of years,' he pleaded, and young Ashypelt who had a particular soft spot for horses, looked round to check the witch was nowhere in sight, and quickly climbed over the dyke.

She felt so sorry for the poor old horse, he was obviously lonely she thought. There was no saddle, so taking handful of his mane, she jumped up and swung herself onto his bony back. It was quite uncomfortable for a start but miraculously, by the second time they circled the paddock, his boniness had disappeared, his mangy coat and the bald patches were fading and there was a sheen to his coat. The mane and tail had grown thick and lustrous and he was holding his big head high and proud, whinnying with the joy of the gallop. After a few minutes, he trotted back to the dyke. She dismounted and bade him goodbye. He thanked her and told her he would help her if he could. And so they parted, he to his grazing and she to her hurrying.

Not too long afterwards the crone arrived at the paddock inquiring for her maid.

> *'Have ye seen a maid o' mine, goin' along this road,*
> *With a long wig-wag, and a long leather bag.*
>
> *And all my gold and silver?'*

'Aye, I saw her, a pretty young lassie. She was here, and she came into the field. I think she was trying to bury something over there but when she saw you in the distance, she left it and ran away.'

The horse indicated something dark over in the middle of the field, and the witch once again found herself climbing a dyke to get her bag back. After much huffing and puffing she managed to get herself over the high dyke and limped off to the middle of the field. Her eyesight, as already mentioned, was very poor, so when she got close to the dark patch in the grass she bent down to see if it was her bag. It wasn't, it was a great big horse poo, and worse still, the horse had followed her over the field. As she bent down, he turned and kicked her viciously on the bottom. She landed right in the horse poo, face first. She was furious, and threatened to have the horse shot when she came back. The horse, being a very wise old horse said nothing but followed her back over the field. And as she attempted to climb the dyke, he very helpfully swivelled about and lashed out with his two hind hooves, thus helping her over the dyke.

Once again she found herself flying higher, much higher than required, clearing the dyke by four or five feet, without the aid of a broomstick. After quite a few minutes, moaning and groaning, she managed to struggle to her feet, limping with pain, and hobbled off in a very hobbling way.

Ashypelt meantime was nearly at the gate. Seeing the gate in front of her, she attempted to open it. But the old gate was very rusty and she could hardly move it, so deciding to climb over it instead. She had just gotten one foot on the lowest bar, when to her surprise the gate spoke to her.

'Swing upon me, won't you please swing upon me, I haven't been swung on for hundreds of years. I loved it when the children would swing on me coming home from school. Won't you please swing upon me?' the gate pleaded.

Ashypelt had always loved to swing on the gates of her father's gardens and she well remembered the simple pleasure it gave.

'Oh yes please,' she replied enthusiastically, 'but

quickly for a wicked witch is chasing me, and she may catch me if I don't hurry.' She quickly climbed upon the gate. As if by some miracle the rusted old gate swung free, back and forth, back and forth; with Ashypelt giggling and laughing, obviously enjoying the swinging sensation and the reminders of her childhood that swinging on the gate brought back. Suddenly the gate slammed shut.

'Hurry little one,' he said urgently, 'hide in those bushes, for I can see the witch in the distance. But keep a close watch and, whatever happens, if she should drop her magic wand, grab it quickly.'

So Ashypelt found herself hiding in the bushes, trembling with fear in case the wicked old crone found her first.

At last the witch limped up to the gate, for she was very sore indeed, her gruntle had never been so disgruntled, and she was in a foul mood.

'Have ye seen a maid o' mine, goin' along this road,
With a long wig-wag, and a long leather bag.
And all my gold and silver?'

'I did indeed,' replied the gate, 'you'll have to be quick though. She was over me and away before I knew what was happening,' he lied.

'Great,' the witch replied, 'open up and let me through then, so I can catch the little madam.'

The gate laughed, which made the witch even more

furious. 'Open up at once, you useless lump of scrap metal, or I'll have you melted down and made into a toilet receptacle,' she screamed.

'I can't do it you ugly old bat,' he replied disdainfully, 'no matter how much you scream. I've been rusted shut for hundreds of years. Did you ever think to put a little oil on my hinges. Not you, you were too busy making porridge and counting your money and whatever disgusting nonsense you get up to in your cellar. You'll have to climb over like everybody else.' And with that he refused to talk to her any more.

The witch, anxious to catch Ashypelt, began to climb over the gate. But the gate just waited patiently, saying nothing, then when she least expected it, he swung violently and very, very quickly back the way she had come, throwing her into the same patch of briars and thorn bushes that Constance and Isabella had landed in. Like them she too was caught fast and the more she struggled the faster she was caught.

'Quick little one,' the gate shouted, 'see her wand, it's lying on the ground just beside me, grab it now, quickly now.'

Ashypelt dashed out from behind the bushes and lifted the wand. She looked helplessly at the gate.

'What do I do now,' she asked the gate, a frantic edge of panic in her voice.

'Just wave it at her and wish for her to be something

else, anything at all.'

Encouraged by the gate, she closed her eyes and wished with all her might. When she opened her eyes, the witch was gone, there was nothing to be seen.

'What did you wish for,' asked the gate, slightly puzzled.

'I couldn't think of anything, nothing at all, so that's what I wished for, nothing at all,' she explained.

'Well, it seems to have worked and that was a very powerful wish. If you had changed her into a chuckie stone, or a frog, she could have been turned back by another witch sometime in the future. But you can't turn back nothing at all can you? There's nothing there to turn back. She's gone for good.'

Ashypelt laughed with joy and danced around on the grass before jumping on the bars of the gate and swinging back and forth for quite some time. They both enjoyed the swing now that there was no danger of the witch harming them. But eventually Ashypelt begged the gates forgiveness, explaining that she must hurry home now. Her poor mother was starving and her sisters were lost; she must go home, buy some food for her mother and then commence a search for her sisters.

'Ahem,' the gate, cleared his throat, 'about your sisters.'

He sounded embarrassed, 'the witch turned them into

a chuckie stone and a frog. If you turn round you'll find them over beside the briars. Just wave the wand again and wish for them to return.'

Ashypelt did as instructed by the gate and was immediately rewarded with the re-appearance of her sisters. They all jumped for joy, laughing and hugging each other, and then, thanking the gate for his help, they all passed through, closing the gate gently behind them and bidding him farewell, they made for home.

What a joyful reunion it was when the three sisters finally walked up the unkempt driveway to their old home. Their mother must have been looking out for them. Seeing her three beloved girls together she ran down the driveway, crying with joy and they all embraced once again.

That night they feasted right royally on all kinds of good and delicious thing, until each and every one of them declared they were absolutely stuffed and unable to eat another morsel.

Afterwards, as they all sat together quaffing the best wine that money could buy, each of the girls related her story to their mother. And after they were done, realising they owed everything to Ashypelt, they all turned to her, raised their glasses on high and drank a toast to her: the saviour of them all.

'To Ashypelt,' they cried out in unison, and drank to her honour.

'I thank you, and you know I love you all dearly, you mother, and dear Constance and Isabella, but could you all please stop calling me Ashypelt, I have a proper name you know.'

'But we've always called you Ashypelt,' her mystified sisters said, 'you have *another* name? What is it?'

The girls looked at their mother, who knew of course, but said nothing and just smiled and winked at her youngest daughter. And so Ashypelt told them.

They never called her Ashypelt again.

Fin I wis a bairn, aboot five or six year aul, there wis nae computers, TV nor sic like. We hid a, "wireless," a big mahogany cabinet, wi Bakelite knobs ye turned tae tune intae fitiver station ye winted tae hear. There wis a gless panel wi the names o' a' the stations, an fin ye turned the knob, a reid bar wid glide fae ae side tae the ither, until ye'd tuned it in. In atween stations there wis jist an affa lot of whistlin' and bleeping noises. As weel as the BBC stations, like the BBC Home Service, and the Light Programme, there wis a hale dose of foreign stations wi queer names like, Grenoble, Hilversum, Ankara, and Luxembourg. Later on I wis a bit mair curious aboot them, but as a bairn I wis mair interested in, *'Listen with Mother,'* for I likit nithing better than tae listen tae the stories.

Efterwards, never contentit wi jist the yin, I wid fair deeve my mither, asking her ower and ower again tae tell me anither story. I beggit and girnt until she telt me yin, bit mair likely she wid tell me tae ask my Da, or my auntie Lena. My mither's sister Lena hid a hoose across the street fae us and kent a' the stories my mither kent, bit hid ither yins like, 'Bob and His Dog.' As for askin my Da, I soon learnt nae tae bother, for his reply wis aye the same.

'I'll tell ye a story aboot wee Johnny Norrie, he wint up three steps an' intae a paper door-ay.'

265

Noo, I can tell ye, that wis affa frustrating tae a five year aul bairn bit he aye jist lauched and 'at wis 'at.

Onywye, the pint I'm takkin a' day tae get roon tae, is this. Fin my mither did tell me a story, at the end o't she would aye hud oot her closed fist, palm uppermaist and open her fingers wi a flickin motion, like shakkin watter aff her fingertips.

'An' that's my story,' she wid declare tae signal the end.

So, tae kerry on the family tradition, ye'll ken fin I write, 'An' that's my story,' it's the end. Bit I'm getting a bittie aheid o' mysel spikkin aboot the end, fin I hinna even startit, so it micht be a gweed idea tae get a move on.

For a puckle o' years noo, I've been writing and singing Scottish folk sangs, jist for my ain amusement. Weel, 'at's nae quite richt, for they seem tae amuse ither folk as weel as mysel. For me, the great thing aboot folk sangs is that they dinna hae tae be ony particular length. If it's short, it's short, and if it needs a bit mair length tae tell the tale, it can be as lang's ye wint. Fae an artistic pint o' view, if yer writing yer ain sangs that's jist grand, bit the problem is, I've nae got a great memory!

'Och! You wrote it, surely ye can mind on't,' some folk say. Bit the truth is, it's harder tae mind the words o' yer ain sangs. Fin ye listen tae a sang on a record, ye jist sort o' sook it up, bit fin it's yer ain, it disnna seem tae work 'at wye, and

266

there ye hiv it. The short sangs are a' richt bit the lang yins can be an affa bother. It's nae that I'm getting senile or nithing like that... weel, I could be like, but nah, I've jist aye had a bad memory. I've tried a'thing; books on how tae train yer memory, tapes ye listen tae in yer sleep, acupuncture and even hypnotism. There wis ither things, bit I canna mind fit they were! Nithing's worked, 'til I've got tae the stage whaur I'm near feart tae start singing a lang sang in case I canna mind the end.

Weel, ae day I wis speaking tae a lady frien', aye, it's hard tae believe I ken, bit I hiv een or twa, fin she suggested maybe I should see a psychic. I can tell ye, I fair teen the huff!

'I'm nae daft,' I says tae her, 'I've jist got a bad memory.'

'Nah, nah Rab,' she says lauchin, 'nae a psychiatrist, a psychic. It's a different thing athegither.'

It seems I'd jist picked her up wrang – mind you, there micht nae be a richt wye o' picking her up, she's an affa weel built quine. Ye'd maist likely rax yer back. Syne she telt me a' aboot this wifie she gis tae see, fa tells her fortune and gies her advice. I thocht I'd tried a' thing else, I micht as weel gie this a try. If nithing else, it micht gie me the idea for a sang. Weel, the next thing I ken, she's wheekit a phone oot o' her bag and arranged a 'sittin,' wi this clairvoyant wifie. Nae backing oot noo!

On the day o' my appintment I turned up at the wifie's hoose and straicht awa I hid a feeling I'd been there afore. Fit the French cry, 'Déjà vu.' The French, so I've heard, hae a word for jist aboot a'thing. Mind you, thon Dod Bush, President o' America, wis supposed tae hae said, 'The trouble wi the French, is they dinna hae a word for entrepreneur.' Maybe it's nae jist verbatim like, bit ye ken fit I mean.

As I walkit up the path, the feeling o' Déjà Vu got stronger 'til I wis fair convinced I'd been there afore. It wis richt spooky like, bit I rung the doorbell a' the same. Efter a wee whilie, the door opened and a cloud o' smoke wafted oot; followed by an aul wifie wi a fag in her mou, wha glowered at me. Truth tae tell, I got thon, 'Déjà vu,' thing even mair, for I seemed tae ken her face.

'Michty, is yer hoose on fire, wifie?' I askit, a bitty concerned, bit she jist ignored me.

'Come in min. Ye'd be the lad wi the bad memory ur ye?' she croaked.

'Aye, that's me richt enough,' I replied, gasping for breath as she led me doon a smoke filled, nicotine stained hallway, intae a smoke filled, nicotine stained front room.

The place wis in near-darkness and in the gloamin I could jist mak oot twa or three chairs, a roon table wi a crystal ba' an' some ither bits an' pieces on't. She hoastit twa or three times and pinted wi a wizened yalla finger tae a chair at ae side o' a roon table. Sittin doon on a chair at the ither side o' the table, she fixed me wi a piercing glare through the curtain o' smoke risin' fae the fag in her mou.

'Ye've aye hid a bad memory,' she said, a bittie grumpy wi it I thocht.

'Aye,' I admitted, impressed, despite my growin asphyxiation.

'It's been much worse lately though, hisn't it?' she said, glowering at me worse than iver, as if I'd done something unforgivable, like opening a windae.

'Aye,' I said again, fair dumfoonert, 'Bit how dae you ken?'

Saying nithin, she pit doon her fag in an ashtray fair chokit wi fag ends and, standing up, leant ower the table and gied me an almichty skelp on the lug! If I wis dumfoonert afore I was mair dumfoonert noo and jumpit tae my feet wi the shock o' it a'.

'Here wifie, I didnae come here tae be bad used. I'm a merriet man – I can get skelpit at hame for nithing,' I protestit, 'Fit dae ye think ye're up tae?'

'I'm yer mither fool, at's fit wye I ken. Ye hinna been near my door for near 10 year. A body could be deid and ye'd niver ken,' she fair skirled at me.

'I thocht ye wis deid,' I said lamely, adding diplomatically 'Bit I'm richt gled I wis wrang.'

It wis my mither, richt enough, aulder, mair wizened, and a bittie yalla roon the edges, bit her a' the same. I hid

269

the good sense tae tell her I wis sorry like, bit she grumped and muttered for as lang as it took her tae licht anither fag.

'So, ye wint help wi yer memory?' And nae waitin for a reply, added 'aboot time an'a.'

I jist noddit, lug still dirlin fae the skelp

'Weel, let me think noo, fit wid be best for ye?' she said, speakin tae hersel an' sorting through the various bits and pieces on the table. 'I winna bother wi the tea leaves. I hinna had muckle luck wi the tea leaves since aboot 1975,' she declared.

'Fit wye nae?' I enquired, innocent like, 'fit happened in 1975 tae mak ye loss yer ability, yer powers?'

'Nah nah, I lost nithin, bit 'at's fin yer Da started buying tea bags.'

She lauched wheezily at her ain joke, then added wistfully, 'it's a dying airt ye ken, reading the tea leaves.'

'I can weel believe 'at,' says I, choking back a hysterical need tae breathe, 'fit are ye gan tae dae then?'

'Nae the Tarot cards onywye and I'm nae readin' yer palm neither. I'm ower close tae ye and I micht jist see things I wint for ye, rither than gie ye a true readin'. Nah, I think I'll hae tae try and contact the ither side and see fit the spirits hiv tae say.'

'Spirits... say...,' I repeated, sounin' like a gype even tae mysel.

'Aye, 'at's fit I said,' she replied, as if speakin tae a

270

bairn. 'The spirits winna care if ye're my son and they'll gie ye advice wi'oot fear nor favour.'

'OK mither, fit iver ye say, bit lets jist get on wi it afore I jine yer spirits.' My een were fair nippin and my throat sair wi the fag-reek.

'Richt... noo, I need ye tae be affa quiet and concentrate,' she warned, 'for I'll be gan intae a trance tae contact the ither side.'

'Hiv ye got a spirit guide?' I askit her.

'Better than 'at laddie,' she said prood kind, 'I've got twa.'

'Dinna tell me – a reid Indian, and a Chinaman,' I surmised. 'Fit wye are spirit guides aye reid Indians and Chinamen?'

'I dinna ken, it's jist aye been like 'at,' says she, 'bit it'll be the Chinaman the day I jalouse.'

'Fit wye dae ye ken, fit's happened tae the reid Indian?' my interest growin.

'Ach, I dinna ken, t'wis jist ae day he disappeart, and I've niver heard fae him syne. I think he must've got lost,' she explained, nae seein the irony in fit she'd jist said. Finally I managed tae speak.

'Mither, only you could hae a reid Indian guide that's got lost.'

'Ach, it's 'a richt, he wis a bit o' a boozer onywye. He wis aye gan on aboot firewater.'

'Oh dearie me, a spirit wi a liking for the booze. It gets worse and worse. Let's jist get on wi it,' I pleaded.

'A' richt, bit mind noo, quiet and concentration, so I can slip intae a trance.' Hivin warned me again, she sat there for a while, heid slumpit as if sleeping. Her breathing, or wheezin' mair like, became deeper and deeper, nae tae mention louder. Nithing happened and I sat there for aboot five minutes listening to her wheeze. I thocht she'd fa'n asleep richt enough. Finally I spoke quietly, nae wintin tae cause her ony shock.

'Are ye sleepin' mither, or are ye in a trance?'

"Nae yet, bit I'm driftin awa,' she said.

'Aye fine, an' I'm richt gled tae hear it, bit 'at smoke's fair driftin awa intae my een.' As I said it, I leant ower the table and nippit the fag oot o' her hand adding, 'Mither, 'em fags are gan tae be the death o' ye.'

She hardly noticed and kerriet on wheezin'. Efter anither wee while, her breathin wis even mair shalla, and seemed tae stop athegither. I wis jist winderin if I should dial '999' for an ambulance, fin she gave an almichty shudder and sat bolt upricht, starin intae fit iver she wis starin intae. She shuddered again and, gaspit a bit, syne settled doon. I waitit again and efter a wee while she said casually.

'OK, ye can ask yer questions noo.'

I hid bin expectin some theatrical flim-flam, an' I wis a bit te'en aback by how ordinary it a' wis.

272

'Eh...aye... can ye help me wi my bad memory? Fin I write a lang sang I can niver mind the words fin I'm singin it. Can ye suggest onnything that micht help?'

There wis a lang silence, bit finally she cleared her throat and spoke.

'I'm in contact wi my Chinaman spirit guide, an he's thinking aboot it. It micht tak a whilie, for he's affa particler and likes tae think aboot it fae a' the angles. He's affa cliver, even though he his got sticky-oot lugs.'

'Fit's sticky-oot lugs got tae dae wi it?' I askit.

'Weel, yer da's cousin Edwin hid affa sticky oot lugs, bit naebody could iver say he wis cliver. Nah, he wis fair gleckit! I widna like ye tae think my Chinaman wis as gleckit as Edwin.'

'I niver gave it a thocht,' I assured her. 'Edwin could niver be mistaken for a Chinaman. He's niver been further than ten mile fae Auchnagatt in his hale life.'

'Nah, bit his mither his,' she said slyly and changed the subject, leavin anither reputation in tatters an' anither faimily mystery in her wake.

'I winder fit's keeping 'at Chinaman - he'll hae nippit aff for a cup o' tea again. Affa fond o' their tea the Chinese, ye ken,' she said, displaying the family trait of, 'surmising,' at first hand.

If 'surmising' wis an Olympic event, my mither wid hae a cabinet fair stappit wi' gold medals. 'He'll be ower on the ither side, sittin doon in his big hoose, wi a' they concubines, drinkin tea in the lap o' luxury, an' us sitting here waitin for an answer.'

'Concubines and a big hoose? Weel, spik aboot getting yer reward in hivin – he must've been an affa special kinda cheil fin he wis livin' tae end up wi 'at. Fit wis he, ane o' they Ming dynasty emperors, or Ghengis Khan, or sic like?'

'I dinna ken. He's jist a Chinaman fa gies me a help fae time tae time, an' I've niver askit his name. It's nane o' my business.'

'Ye mean, ye've niver thocht tae ask, even yince in a' the years he's bin yer guide. Dearie me, Mither, 'at's shockin,' I said in mock disbelief.

'I hiv askit him, bit he aye jist says he's confused and I dinna like tae embarrass him by gaen on aboot it,' she explained.

'Weel, maybe fin he comes back fae ha'en his fly cup, we can speir at him again,' I suggested.

This time there wis nae reply, her heid noddit ontae her chest again, and the hivvy breathin re-commenced. Efter a while, a lang while, she showed some signs o' comin roon, so I spoke tae her again.

'Is 'at Chinaman nae back fae his tea break yet? It's affa like phonin BT and being put on hud, bit wi'oot the benefit o' Mozart's electronic symphony.'

'Wheesht min,' she said, looking richt at me, bit kinda

through me at the same time. I lookit roon tae see if there wis onnybody ahin me, but there wis nithin. I got a wee shiver doon my back, like somebody hid jist 'walked across my grave' as my faither used tae say.

'He's back,' she announced, 'I can see him sittin, cross-leggit on a big pilla, looking affa happy wi himself.'

'Nah! I dinna believe it, he's jist bin ha'en his efterneen tea, surrounded by a hale jing-bang o' bonny Chinese lassies. Fit's he got tae be happy aboot?'

'Dinna be nesty noo, there's nae need for 'at,' she chided, 'Onnywye, I think he's got some advice for ye.'

'Speir fit 'is name is first mither. I'd like tae ken, if I'm gan tae tak his advice seriously.'

'Aye, aye, nae bother, I'll jist ask him noo.'

There wis a wee delay while she passed on my request.

'It's jist the same answer again – he says he's confused. He's a richt fine aul mannie an' I dinna like tae embarrass him. He's getting on a bit noo; he's been in the spirit for a lang time, an' he's maybe jist forgot.'

'Or maybe wi him being Chinese yer nae pickin his name up richt. Speir at him again, jist tae mak sure,' I urged her.

'Richt, I'll try yince mair, bit that's it. He'll be thinkin I'm jist an ill-mannert lassie wi nae respect for her elders.' Reluctantly, she tried again.

'Nah, it's jist the same answer again... he's

confused... nah.. nah.... hud on... nah... hud on.. hud on... aye... he's nae confused at a'... got ye noo... he's nae confused, he's Confucious!' She declared in triumph, and then added. 'Fa's Confucious?'

'Confucious was a great Chinese sage and philosopher, born aboot 551BC in Lu province, in what is now modern day Shangdong,' I replied. 'Yer richt, he *is* gettin on a bit. Mind you, twa and a half thoosand years o' tea and concubines wid age onny man.'

'Fit wye dae ye ken 'at?' she askit. 'Aboot Confucious I mean, nae aboot concubines.'

'I read a lot.'

'Weel, stop it. Nae winder ye canna mind onythin. Yer heid's fair stappit wi useless rubbitch.'

'Fitiver ye say mither,' I agreed.

Onnythin for a quiet life I thocht, bit gettin back tae the subject, I askit, 'So fit words o' wisdom dis the great Confucious hae tae offer me?'

'Wait a meenit an' I'll ask him,' she replied, ga'in a' wheezy again. 'He wints tae spik tae ye himsel. Files he jist passes on a message, bit he's been listenin, an' he's affa pleased that ye ken fa' he is efter he's been deid a' this time, so he wants tae tell ye himsel'. Fit an honour.' She fair swelled wi pride as she said it.

'Weel, ye can tell him I am indeed honoured that one of the greatest men in the history o' the human race his ta'en the time tae help me wi my problem. I'm affa grateful for his help, like.'

'Hud on... he's jist comin through.' And wi these words I wis in contact wi the great Confucious himsel'.

Her een stared straicht aheid, her features distortit, and at first jist a queer gurgling noise came oot o' her mou. A few mair breaths and Confucious spoke through my aul mither, as clear as could be. In a strange sing-song accent, he imparted his thochts direct tae me.

'Confucious he say, man with short memory, no writee long songs.'

Stunned by the wisdom o' the, 'advice,' I sat there wi a guppy-like expression on my face.

'Is there onnythin ye'd like tae add?' I askit, trying tae draw oot same mair pearls o' wisdom, but efter a few seconds silence, my mither started tae come roon.

'Weel, fit did he say? Wis it onny help?' She wis like a wee lassie; a' excitit and wintin tae hear fit the great man hid said. I jist couldnae tell her the truth.

'I'm affa sorry, bit I canna tell ye mither. He made me promise niver tae tell fit he said, bit I can tell ye noo, it's been a great help tae me. An' it's a' thanks tae you, an' 'at's something I'll niver forget,' I said truthfully.

She wis richt pleased wi hersel, an' so we hid a cup o' tea and spoke aboot aul times. As I wis leavin I gave her a wee cuddle and a kiss and telt her I'd come back in twa or

277

three days tae see how she wis getting on.

Walkin doon the path, I cast my mind back tae fit Confucious hid said and the soun o' him gigglin efter he said it. Maybe he jist wintit tae get his ain back for a' the thoosands o' bad jokes in his name ower the years. Fitivir his reasons, I wis mair trickit than onythin else. Somethin in the fact that a twa an' a half thoosand year aul Chinaman still hid a sense o' humour and hid shared a joke, even though it wis at my expense, wis worth a' the trauchle I'd been through this afterneen. I hid a wee lauch tae mysel fae time tae time as I drove hame.

An' that's my story!

Issues of 'translation.'

When writing in Scots/Doric there is always the vexed question of spelling to be taken into account. Even using the 'recognised' spelling conventions may not give the true flavour of the language. Take for instance the word 'guid.' Some people will ignore the spelling and just read it as 'good,' others will say 'gid', but the pronunciation in the North East of Scotland is 'gweed,' as in the Spanish name 'Guido.' We have tried to retain the flavour and sounds of the language by using a more phonetic spelling for some of the words.

The 'flow' and vivacity of the oral tradition can be weakened, even destroyed, when at attempt is made to transcribe and preserve it as written prose. We have tried as far as possible to hold onto the original spirit of oral storytelling while 'tweaking' punctuation for the written word. We have also tried as much as possible to get rid of the 'Scottish,' apostrophe.

We appreciate it will never be possible to please all but hope that, for the many, the uniqueness and vibrancy of the stories will excuse any perceived failings in final written delivery.

DEVERON PRESS

The Deveron Press was established by James Leatham (1865-1945) in 1916. Leatham himself was a native of the North East and settled in Turriff in that year, after a lifetime of travel in the print and publishing business. A century on, in tribute to Leatham and his principles, The Deveron Press was reborn and the Centenary Collection published. It comprises ten classic works either written by or published by Leatham during his lifetime.

Leatham said *'publishing is an adventure'* and in that spirit the new Deveron Press looks forward as well as back.

In 2017 we published work by North East writers Pat Hutchison and John Barron as well as a volume by Lachlan Munro on Robert Bontine Cunninghame Graham.

For more information about The Deveron Press and our current publications please visit our website:

www.thedeveronpress.scot

You can buy our books direct online from

www.unco.scot

and from a range of online and 'real' book retailers.